Philosophy, Technology,
and the Arts
in the Early Modern Era

Philosophy, Technology, and the Arts in the Early Modern Era

by Paolo Rossi

Translated by Salvator Attanasio
Edited by Benjamin Nelson

HARPER TORCHBOOKS
Harper & Row, Publishers
New York, Evanston, and London

HARPER TORCHBOOKS/Advisory Editor in the Humanities and Social Sciences: BENJAMIN NELSON

PHILOSOPHY, TECHNOLOGY, AND THE ARTS IN THE
EARLY MODERN ERA

The first chapter of *I Filosofi e le Macchine* is a revision and amplification of the essay "*Sulla valutazione delle arti mechaniche nei secoli XVI e XVII*" ("On the Appraisal of the Mechanical Arts in the Sixteenth and Seventeenth Centuries") published in *Rivista critica di storia della filosofia* (1956, 2). The second and third appendixes were published, in a different form, in *Rivista di filosofia* (1955, 2) and in *Rivista critica di storia della filosofia* (1957, 1) respectively.

First edition: HARPER TORCHBOOKS, 1970
Harper & Row, Publishers, Inc.
New York, N.Y. 10016.

Library of Congress Catalog Card Number: 70-103055

To Andreina, Mario, and Anna

CONTENTS

Preface   ix

1. Mechanical Arts and Philosophy
   in the Sixteenth Century   1

2. The Idea of Scientific Progress   63

3. Philosophy, Technics, and the History
of the Arts in the Seventeenth Century   100

Appendixes

I. The Nature-Art Relationship and
   the Machine of the World   137

II. Truth and Utility in the Science
    of Francis Bacon   146

III. The New Science
and the Symbol of Prometheus   174

Index   187

PREFACE

━━━━━━━━━━◆◆◆◆◆━━━━━━━━━━

*"The passages which follow concerning the use of me-
chanical arts are plain enough. Certainly human life is
much indebted to them, for very many things which concern both the furniture of religion and the ornament of
state and the culture of life in general, are drawn from
their store. And yet out of the same fountain come instruments of lust, and also instruments of death."*
FRANCIS BACON, *Daedalus sive mechanicus*, 1609

There are clearly discernible links between several broad
themes of European culture and the debate on the mechanical arts which assumed a singular intensity of character in
the years between 1400 and 1700. A new view of labor, of
the function of technical knowledge, and of the significance
of artificial processes through which nature was altered and
transformed clearly makes its way into the work of artists
and experimentalists of the fifteenth century and into the
treatises of engineers and technicians of the sixteenth century. This trend is discernible even at the level of philosophy: in those social groups which were much taken up
with problems of this type, there emerged an appraisal of
the arts that was quite different from the one which had
traditionally prevailed. It was now argued that some of the
methods employed by technicians and artisans to modify
and alter nature might also be useful for acquiring a real
knowledge of natural reality. Indeed, as was boldly asserted
in an explicit disputation with the traditional philosophies,
the newer methods might have the distinct merit of exhibiting nature in motion.
The defense of the mechanical arts against the charge of
baseness, and the rejection of the notions that culture coin-

cides with the horizon of the liberal arts and that practical operations are tantamount to servile labor, in reality implied the rejection of a certain conception of science, namely, of science as a disinterested contemplation of truth, as an investigation that comes into being and is pursued only *after* the things necessary to life have been attended to.

Exponents of the other revolt, directed against every form of occult and arcane wisdom, against the very ancient sacerdotal conception of knowledge—widespread in the technical literature of that time—often joined forces with those whose polemical writings aimed to undermine and dislodge the established Aristotelian doctrine. Writers on technical subjects and natural philosophers both stressed one point: knowledge has a public and collaborative character. It presents itself as a series of individual contributions organized in the form of a systematic discourse, which is offered with a general success in view and which in turn ought properly to be the patrimony of all mankind.

This view of knowledge and science—the first traces of which have been sought in the works of the technicians of the late sixteenth century—played a decisive and determining role in the formation and development of the idea of scientific progress. The men who toiled in the workshops, in the arsenals, and in the studios, or those who had dropped their disdain of practice, considered the operations conducted on these premises a form of cognition. Moreover, they arrived at a theoretical conception of their work which assigned ends to it that were very different and certainly more impersonal than individual sanctity or literary immortality. On the other hand, the sense of the further perfectibility of one's own work, the assertion of the necessity of intellectual cooperation and of the progressive character of a knowledge that grows on itself in the course of time, enriching itself through the joint work of many hands, and the recognition of the ever new results achieved by the arts led to the assertion that the cultural horizon of the ancients was a limited one. It also led these early experimenters to lay stress on the provisional and historical character of the discoveries and truths of the antique world.

This theme, on which the humanists of the fifteenth century had dwelt at length, was coupled with the attribution of universal value to several typical categories of technical knowledge—for example, cooperation, progressiveness, perfectibility, and invention. In this way the philosophical culture of the seventeenth century brought on a full and mature awareness of certain ideas that had slowly been making their way at the edges of the official culture, outside the academic culture, and almost always in opposition to it. As a result, not a few of the greatest exponents of seventeenth-century philosophy became the interpreters of certain vital and pressing needs present in the historical reality of modern Europe. It is in this sense that, in the following pages, we have dealt with the texts bearing on the great debate between the ancients and the moderns.

In our discussion of Bruno, Descartes, Galileo, Gassendi, and Leibniz, we have not gone beyond a consideration, perforce summary at times, of the impact which the new appraisal of techniques and the mechanical arts had on the prevailing concepts of nature, philosophy, and science.

But no matter how we may view the subject, what is certain is that the idea of knowledge as construction, the postulation of the model machine for the explanation and comprehension of the physical universe, the image of God as a clockmaker, and the thesis that man can truly know what he fashions or constructs and *only* what he fashions or constructs, are all assertions closely connected with the penetration of the philosophical and scientific world by that new mode of considering practice and operations to which we have already referred.

The discussion concerning the mechanical arts, the relations between techniques and science, and the function and tasks of technology has certainly not been brought to a close in contemporary culture. The image of an atomic city of our time, surrounded by armed guards, in no wise calls

to mind the cities governed by scientists and ruled by reason, the free academies projected and hoped for three centuries ago by many of the pioneers and theorists of the new
sciences. In most cases the "natural philosophers" of our
time have had to work in environments quite different from
that of Solomon's House. A research based on secrecy rather
than on collaboration and on the public character of the
results, whose aim is the power of a state or of a social
group rather than the well-being of the whole human race,
a technics reduced to thaumaturgy or to an instrumental
subsidy of a superstitious view of the world, an exploitation
of nature based on the exploitation of man—these are features that are doubtlessly closer to the ideals espoused by
Agrippa and Cardano than to those of Bacon and Galileo.
Our investigation, which aspires to be only a chapter in a
history which was fated to become increasingly more complex in the course of the last two centuries, can nevertheless
serve a useful purpose by clarifying the meaning of certain
terms and the genesis, often remote in time, of the recur-
rent problems which are still the subjects of passionate
debate today.

Chapter One

Mechanical Arts and Philosophy
in the Sixteenth Century

1.

In the "Notice to Readers" that served as a preface to his *Discours admirables* published in 1580, Bernard Palissy, the famous French potter, posed a characteristic question to himself: Is it possible that a man can know something and be knowledgeable about natural effects without having read books written in Latin by philosophers?[1] Palissy was an apprentice glassmaker who achieved great fame through his quest for the secret of a famous white enamel. He designed many machines during his adventurous life, but he never successfully carried out any of his projects. He risked death many times through starvation or judicial sentence. He died in the Bastille, either in 1589 or 1590. In the *Discours*, which is one long invective against the culture of the professors at the Sorbonne, we find philosophy identified as the art of observing nature and the assertion that this art is in no way the exclusive patrimony of learned men and philosophers. It ought, rather, to be spread among all the earth's

[1]A. France, *Les oeuvres de B. Palissy publiées d'après les textes originaux avec une notice historique et bibliographique* (Paris, 1880), p. 166. This edition contains, among others, reprints of: *Discours admirables* (Paris, 1580); *Recepte véritable par laquelle tous les hommes de France pourront apprendre à multiplier leurs thrésors. Item ceux qui n'ont jamais eu cognoissance des lettres pourront apprendre une philosophie nécessaire à tous les habitants de la terre* (La Rochelle, 1553).

inhabitants, and it can be born only of a "cult of things" which violently rejects bookish culture and philosophical tradition.[2]

Palissy replied affirmatively to the question that he had posed to himself:

Through practice I prove that the theories of many philosophers, even the most ancient and famous ones, are erroneous in many points. Anyone can ascertain this for himself in two hours merely by taking the trouble to visit my workshop. Marvelous things can be seen here (demonstrated and proved in my writings and arranged in an orderly manner with texts at the bottom so that the visitor may be his own instructor). I assure you, dear reader, that you will learn more about natural history from the facts contained in this book than you would learn in fifty years devoted to the study of the theories of the ancient philosophers.[3]

This preface, whose patent naïveté in no sense lessens its significance, contained the embryo of two central ideas of Francis Bacon's philosophy: it is necessary to replace the cult of books by the cult of nature and thereby to restore the possibility of a fruitful "commerce of the mind with things."

The purpose of Palissy's museum of natural objects, by which he illustrated his book, was not to amuse readers or to arouse their curiosity. Rather, it aimed to be a means of study, a potentially powerful instrument of scientific explication and research. It is probable that the sixteen-year-old Bacon, during his sojourn in Paris, attended the public lectures which Palissy delivered on agriculture, mineralogy, and geology; and perhaps Bacon had precisely Palissy's case in mind when in the *Novum organum* he wrote: "Except when it occasionally happens that some workman of acute wit and covetous of honor applies himself to a new invention; which he does mostly at the expense of his fortunes."[4]

[2]On Palissy, cf. L. Audiat, *B. Palissy* (Paris, 1864); E. Dupuy, *B. Palissy* (Paris, 1894).

[3]A. France, *Les oeuvres de B. Palissy*, p. 166.

[4]Palissy's influence on Bacon was argued by A. B. Hanschmann, *B. Palissy und F. Bacon* (Leipzig, 1903). The hypothesis was taken up again by Sir T. Clifford Allbutt, "Palissy, Bacon and the Revival

Palissy certainly was not a cultured man; he was but a humble artisan who apparently had read Vitruvius and some treatises by Paracelsus and Cardano.[5] Palissy was an exponent of the thesis, carried to its extreme consequences, that the book of nature is extraordinarily richer and more complex than any other book. This thesis, already implicit in the polemic that Erasmus and Montaigne had directed against the pedants, was to be energetically resumed by the English Baconian group and by Robert Boyle. Palissy, however, subverted it by asserting a "scientific primitivism" which rejected books in the name of nature and theory for an empiricism as exhibited on an artisan level.[6] But Palissy's violent polemic against the despisers of the mechanical arts and manual labor drew its strength precisely from this form of primitivism. Not accidentally, his invective assumed the characteristics of a political position and of a violent protest against social injustice.

Many eat of their incomes in acts of bravado and unnecessary expenses and in the retinue of the Court, in ostentatious attire, or other things. Such people would find it much more useful to eat onions with their peasants and by teaching the latter to live properly, by setting a good example for them, by preventing them from ruining themselves with litigations, and by themselves tilling the soil, by digging ditches and by holding themselves in readiness, at the opportune time, for service to the Sovereign in defense of the homeland. Certain young blades,

---

of Natural Science," *Proceedings of the British Academy* (1913–14), Vol. VI, pp. 232ff., and by B. Farrington, *F. Bacon, Philosopher of Industrial Science* (New York, 1941). Farrington amplified his observations on this point in his article "On Misunderstanding the Philosophy of Bacon," in *Science, Medicine and History, Essays in Honour of Charles Singer* (Oxford, 1953), vol. I, pp. 439–50. The passage from Bacon is in *Novum organum*, I, 84.

[5]P. Duhem, *Etudes sur Leonardo da Vinci* (Paris, 1906), Vol. I, pp. 223–53, has shown how Palissy, despite his ironic comments on Cardano, was influenced by the French translation of *De subtilitate: les livres de H. Cardanus par Richard Le Blanc* (Paris, 1556).

[6]For the significance of these positions: W. E. Houghton, "The History of Trades: Its Relation to Seventeenth Century Thought," in *Roots of Scientific Thought*, ed. P. Wiener and A. Noland (New York, 1957), pp. 379–80.

however, consider that they would be dishonored by wielding an agricultural implement. A gentleman, impoverished and up to his ears in debt, thinks he is transformed into a peasant if he wields a pitchfork or a hoe.[7]

Robert Norman was an English sailor who, after almost twenty years at sea, devoted his energies to the manufacture and sale of compasses. One year after the publication of Palissy's *Discours*, he published, in London, a little book on magnetism and the declination of the magnetic needle.[8] Norman described himself as an "unlearned mathematician" who in the exercise of his profession had gathered data on the magnet and the "strange and newe propertie of declinying." Casting aside the reservations born of his lack of culture, he decided to risk his good name and defy the calumnies of his adversaries and the criticisms of gossips in order "to propose to the consideration of the world" the results of his reflections and experiments. Norman claimed to have worked for the greater glory of God and for England's advantage, and admonished the reader constantly to bear in mind that he was but a simple mariner and that he "will not offer to dispute with the logitians," nor give a satisfactory explanation of the "naturall causes" of terrestrial magnetism.

The modesty of Norman's approach did not prevent him from arriving at significant results. William Gilbert was to make frequent references to the *Newe Attractive*, as well as generous use of the results achieved by "this expert mariner and ingenious artisan." Despite his caution and his deferential attitude toward the culture of "learned men," Norman had a clear sense of the difference and the fundamental

[7]A. France, *Les oeuvres de B. Palissy*, p. 90.

[8]*The Newe Attractive, containing a short discourse of the Magnes or Lodestone and amongest others his vertues, of a newe discovered secret and subtil propertie concernying the declinying of the needle* (London, 1581). This book was republished in 1585, 1592, 1596, 1614, 1720. The last edition is included in G. Hellmann, *Rara Magnetica* (Berlin, 1898). The passages quoted are from Norman's preface.

opposition that existed between his investigations based on things and not words ("not regarding the wordes, but the matter") and the knowledge of bookmen who were incapable of appreciating the work of "Mechanitians":

But I doe verily thinke, that notwithstanding the learned in the Sciences, being in their studies amongst their books, can imagine greate matters, and set downe their farre fetched conceits in faire flowe, and with plentiful wordes, wishing that all Mechanitians were such, as for want of utterance, should be forced to deliver unto them their knowledge and conceits, that they might flourish uppon them, and applye them at their pleasures: yet there are in this land diverse Mechanitians, that in their severall faculties and professions have the use of those Arts at their fingers endes. And can applye them to their severall purposes, as effectionately and more readily than those who woulde most condemne them.

The philosophers, the exponents of the official culture, according to Norman, therefore deny that the observations of the technicians and artisans had any meaning or validity. The latter's knowledge was formed autonomously, so the unlearned must of necessity convey a precise invitation to the men of culture: "Therefore, I woulde wish the learned to use modestly in publishing their conceits, and not disdainfully to condemne men that will search out the secrets of the *Artes* and professions, and publish the same to the behoofe and use of others, no more than they woulde that others should judge of them, for promising much and performing little or nothing at all."

We find these same concepts expressed with less naïveté but with a comparable energy by a professional philosopher, Juan Luis Vives, a friend of Erasmus and of Thomas More. He was a tutor at the English court, a man of great learning who addressed his writings to the cultured and often refined public of the humanist circles of that time. In *De tradendi disciplines,* Vives invited European scholars to pay serious attention to the technical problems regarding the construction of machines, agriculture, weaving, and navigation. He exhorted them to lower their view to the work of artisans so that they might know "where and how those arts have been invented, practiced, developed, preserved and how they can be applied for our use and benefit." The cultured man must overcome his traditional disdain for common knowledge, and he "must not be ashamed to enter into the workshops and into the factories, asking questions of the artisans and trying to become cognizant of the details of their work." He reminded them that an incredible increase of human wisdom is derived from the work of those who have written their observations on the methods and techniques employed in the individual arts thereby transmitting it to their successors. The knowledge of nature, wrote Vives in *De causis corruptarum artium,* is not entirely in the hands of philosophers and dialecticians. In reality peasants and artisans know her much better than great philosophers (*melius agricolae et fabri norunt quam ipsi tanti philosophi*). Peasants and artisans, he pointed out, operate in nature and on nature. In contrast to philosophers, they have not constructed for themselves a series of imaginary entities to which to attribute a dignified name.

Enraged against nature about whom they knew nothing, the dialecticians have constructed another for themselves; that is to say the nature of formalities, of individualities, of relations, of Platonic ideas and other monstrosities which cannot be understood even by those who have invented them. They attribute a name full of dignity to all these things and they call them metaphysics. If someone has an intelligence which is wholly ignorant of nature, or which has a horror of her, a mind which instead has a bent for abstruse things and foolish dreams, they say that such a person possesses a metaphysical intelligence.[9]

Vives' text appeared in 1531. Two years later, in the *Vie treshorrificante du grand Gargantua,* Rabelais placed the

[9]Juan Luis Vives, *De causis corruptarum artium* (Basileae, 1555), p. 410. On Vives, see C. Vasoli, "Juan Luis Vives e un programma umanistico di riforma della logica," in *Atti dell'Accademia Toscana di Scienze e Lettere La Colombaria,* vol. XXV (1960–61), pp. 219–63 (with copious bibliographical information).

study of the work of artisans among the indispensable elements of a complete education. Under the guidance of Ponocrates, the young Gargantua studied natural science,
arithmetic, geometry, and music, alternating study with the
most varied physical exercises. On cold or rainy days the
pupil studied the arts of sculpture and painting, and teacher
and pupil would then go to see how metals were drawn or
artillery pieces were cast, or they would visit the "goldsmiths, the carvers of precious stones, the alchemists, the
watch makers, the printers, the organ-makers, the dyers."[10]

Palissy, Norman, Vives, and Rabelais, at diverse levels
and with different intentions, voiced the demand, very widespread in the sixteenth century, for a knowledge in which
the observation of phenomena, attention to operations, and
empirical research would have a superior status vis-à-vis
rhetorical evasions, verbal accommodations, logical subtle-
ties, and *a priori* constructions. We find this very demand,
accompanied by a sharp historical awareness and a crude
diagnosis of the perils implicit in every aristocratic and exclusively bookish culture, in one of the great texts of the
new science: the *De humani corporis fabrica* of Andreas
Vesalius (1543). The protest, polemic, and exhortation bear
on the particular situation of a particular branch of knowledge. The degeneration of theory and the debased level of
doctrine appear to be linked to the steadily reinforced separation between technics and sciences and between manual
work and the elaboration of scientific theories:

After the barbarian invasions all the sciences, which before
had gloriously flourished and been rightly practiced, went to
rack and ruin. At that time, and first of all in Italy, the fashionable doctors began to despise the work of the hand, in imitation of the ancient Romans. They assigned the manual treatments, which they considered necessary for their patients, to
slaves and limited themselves to supervising. The methods for
cooking and preparing aliments for the sick were left to nurses,
the dosage of medicines to pharmacists, the manual operations

10Rabelais, Bk. I, Chap. 24.

to barbers. Thus, in the course of time . . . certain doctors, proclaiming themselves physicians, personally arrogated to themserves the prescriptions of medicaments and diets for obscure maladies and abandoned the rest of medicine to those whom they call surgeons and consider hardly better than slaves. In this way, unfortunately, they estranged themselves from the most important and most ancient branch of the art of medicine, that which (granted that there truly is another) is based above all on the investigation of nature. . . . When the whole procedure of the manual operation was handed over to barbers, the doctors not only soon lost the true knowledge of the viscera, but very soon practical anatomy also came to an end. This no doubt was due to the fact that the doctors no longer risked operating; while those to whom this task had been entrusted were too ignorant to read the writings of the teachers of anatomy. . . . Thus it happened that this deplorable division of the medical art has introduced into our schools the odious system, now in vogue, through which one individual performs the dissection of the human body and the other describes the parts. The latter is perched on a high pulpit like a crow and with an air of great disdain, he repeats to the point of monotony accounts concerning facts that he has not directly observed, but has learned by rote from the books of others, or of which he has a description in front of him. The dissectionist, ignorant of the art of speech, is not able to explain the dissection to the students and badly arranges the demonstration that should follow the doctor's explanations, while the doctor never lends a hand to the work itself, but disdainfully guides the ship with the help of the manual worker, and he talks. Thus everything is poorly taught, days are wasted in absurd questions, and the students are confusedly taught less than what a butcher, from his meat-block, could teach the doctor.[11]

Vesalius fought for the convergence in medicine of theory and direct observation. At the same time he polemicized against the figure of the professor whose knowledge is reduced to empty words and the vivisectionist reduced to the status of a butcher. His protest against the "crows" was not an isolated case. In the course of these years, we find in

[11]A. Vesalius, *De humani corporis fabrica* (Basileae, 1543), Preface. See B. Farrington, "Vesalius and the Ruin of Ancient Medicine," *Modern Quarterly* (1938), pp. 23ff.

all the most advanced exponents of European culture the tendency to replace a prevalently literary or rhetorical education by a type of teaching that would give a notable, if not a preponderant position to technical preparation and professional formation. In England, Sir Humphrey Gilbert's *Queen Elizabeth Academy,* written about 1562,[12] was a highly significant example of this tendency. In his work Gilbert dwelt primarily on those aspects of technical instruction which could contribute to the formation of a new type of gentleman capable of being assimilated into the new English society—a type of society in which ability in politics, diplomacy, culture, manners, and competence in military and navigational skills were becoming much more important and decisive elements than the original virtues of blood and birth. The educational program outlined by Gilbert was concerned exclusively with a restricted number from the ruling aristocracy, particularly the younger sons. English was the only language which Gilbert allowed in teaching. The curriculum, which was set in opposition to the theoretical one prevailing in the universities, had to be relevant to "things practical and useful for the present, in peace as well as in war. . . ." The teaching of logic was combined with that of rhetoric, and the rhetorical exercises were intended to equip the student with the necessary skills for the delivery of political orations and military speeches. The task of political philosophy was to study the history of various states, the systems of government, the fiscal systems, and the administration of justice. But it was in the study of natural philosophy and mathematics that the reduction of "physical" knowledge to a knowledge of a technical character, concerning fortifications, strategy, and the use of

[12]Gilbert's work has been published by F. J. Furnivall in the Early English Text Society Series (1869). See also *The Voyages and Colonising Enterprises of Sir H. Gilbert,* Hakluyt Society (1940), vol. 2; On pedagogical work, W. H. Woodward, *La pedagogia del Rinascimento* (Florence, 1923), pp. 298–302; F. Watson, *The Beginning of the Teaching of Modern Subjects in England* (London, 1909).

artillery, clearly predominates. Geography and astronomy were taught in terms of navigation; medicine in terms of first aid and treatment of the wounded. The secrets of nature "will have to be studied in all possible ways" and the results of experiments that have been conducted "will have to be reported on without enigmatic and obscure phrases." A man-of-war and an experimental garden were placed at the disposal of the students. The teaching of law, modern languages, music, fencing, and the dance was to round off the education of the young English gentleman.

Gilbert, better known, and rightly so, as a pioneer of English colonization than as a writer on pedagogy, evidently wished to be a man capable of combining the virtues of a colonizer and a courtier. In reality, Gilbert's intention, like that of many other Englishmen of his time, was to adapt the humanistic ideals of courtesy to the new requirements of Elizabethan society. On the one hand, the aristocracy was prodded to acquire a technico-cultural patrimony which would put it in a valid position to confront the rise of a new social class, men of law and landed proprietors; and on the other hand, humanistic education was presented as a resource for providing this updated aristocracy with the technical knowledge which it needed to win a position for itself at court and in society.[13]

The texts to which we have been referring all go back to the half-century which falls between 1530 and 1580. In the writings of a humble Parisian artisan, a Spanish philosopher, a Flemish scientist linked to the Italian cultural tradition, and an English pioneer of colonization, we have noted the presence of a series of common themes: (1) the procedures of artisans, engineers, and technicians have a value for the ends of the progress of knowledge; (2) such

[13]On this cultural situation see F. Caspari, *Humanism and the Social Order in Tudor England* (Chicago, 1954); P. N. Siegel, "English Humanism and the New Tudor Aristocracy," *Journal of History of Ideas* (1952), p. 4.

procedures are recognized as having the dignity of cultural facts; and (3) men of culture must give up their traditional contempt for "operations" or "practice" and discard every conception of knowledge that is merely rhetorical or contemplative to turn to the observation and study of techniques and the arts.

It was not merely a question of recognizing the dignity of the arts, or their inclusion in programs designed to provide a complete education. In Palissy, Norman, Vives, Vesalius and Gilbert clear indications are found of what was destined to be spread far and wide and to enjoy a singular fortune in the coming era of the new science. Some of the procedures utilized by men to produce utilitarian objects or to build machines, and thus modify or alter nature through the work of their hands, benefited the actual knowledge of natural reality much more than those intellectual constructions and philosophical systems that finally impede or limit man's active exploration.

The polemic against the "pedants" and against bookish learning was subverted into the advocacy of a new type of knowledge. The circulation achieved by these ideas, present in different forms in numerous texts, must not make us think that they were lacking in revolutionary implications in a cultural sense. This appraisal of the mechanical arts, the recognition of a "debt" on the part of scientific learning to the methods of technology (which was to occupy a prominent place in the writings of Bacon, Harvey, Galileo, and Boyle) implied the rejection of that concept of science which, although dubious, had remained alive and operative for centuries: a science which comes into being only when the processes necessary to human life are attended to and which then turns its attention to a disinterested investigation and contemplation of truth. This rejection, as we have seen with Palissy, was not to be without consequence on the level of ethics and politics. Campanella viewed men who do not practice some art useful to human life as "hobos or scum *(excrementa)* of the republic, as are many noble-

men of this age." The Baconian, William Petty, defending
the cultural dignity of the mechanical arts, asserted that
"it often happens that many of those who now guide a plow
could have been capable of governing the State." Diderot,
finally, pointed out that the prejudice according to which
"to turn one's attention to sensible and material objects"
constitutes "a derogation of the dignity of the human spirit"
and has filled the cities "with proud reasoners or useless
contemplatives and the countrysides with ignorant, lazy
and disdainful, petty tyrants."[14]

For a clear awareness of the historical significance of
certain violent attitudes and of certain passionate "de-
fenses," it is useful to bear in mind that these polemics were
not only directed against the past, or tradition. For many
centuries the contempt that was felt for manual workers
had been "transferred" to manual activity as such, and now
the latter appeared last on the scale of social values and
was excluded from the sphere of cultural values. These concepts were still accepted in the seventeenth century and
even later. To convince ourselves of this, we need only
recall how the French Jesuits were scandalized by what
they thought was an excessive number of articles on technical subjects in Diderot's *Encyclopédie*. Indeed, without
looking far ahead, we can open Richelet's *Dictionnaire
français* (1680) and turn to the article entitled "Mécha-
nique": "This term, speaking of particular arts, signifies
that which is the opposite of liberal and honorable; it has
the connotation of baseness and of being little worthy of an
honest person." It was not a question of a mere perpetua-
tion of certain linguistic usages. In 1613 the jurist Charles
Loyseau codified some widespread convictions when he
asserted that "artisans are considered ignoble persons" or

[14]Campanella, *Aforismi politici*, ed. Firpo (Turin, 1941), p. 161;
W. Petty, *The Advice of W. Petty to Mr. Samuel Hartlib for the
Advancement of some particular part of Learning* (1648), repub-
lished in *The Harleian Miscellany* (1808–1811), vol. VI, p. 144;
Diderot, "Art," in *Encyclopédie ou dictionnaire raisonné des sciences,
des arts et de métiers*.

"that which is base and despicable is commonly called mechanical." His statements concerning peasants, which also reflected an ancient bucolic tradition, are equally significant: "There is no life more innocent than theirs, nor a gain greater than theirs, according to nature . . . but they are considered base to such a degree that we marvel to see that some of them still exist to nourish us."[15] Montaigne, Locke, and La Bruyère had talked about the peasants of France with equal realism, although with quite different intentions.[16] Behind the attribution of baseness to the activity of artisans, "mechanics," and peasants, stood a very particular concept of human labor and of its significance in terms of this world and the world beyond. Turning to Richelieu's *Testament politique* (1642), we can see how a definite political conception emerged from a certain type of appraisal of human labor: "If the lower classes are too much at ease, it is impossible to keep them within the rules of their duty. They must be compared to those mules who, accustomed to their burden, are ruined more because of a long rest than because of toil."[17]

Aristotle had excluded "mechanical workers" from the category of citizens and had differentiated them from slaves on the basis that the former attended to the needs of several persons, while the latter took care of only a single person. Thus the opposition between slaves and freemen tended to break down on the basis of technique and science; that is, between a knowledge oriented toward practice and use, immersed in material and useful objects, and rational

[15]Cf. L. Febvre, "Travail, évolution d'un mot et d'une idée," *Journal de Psychologie*, vol. I (1948), p. 23.

[16]Cf. P. Jaccard, *Histoire sociale du travail de l'antiquité à nos jours* (Paris, 1960), pp. 183–84. "This fellow digging in my garden has just buried his father. . . . They go to sleep only to die" (Montaigne, 1580). "You see wild animals, male and female, scattered through the countryside, black, livid and burned by the sun, tied to the soil that they dig and turn over with an invincible stubbornness" (La Bruyère, 1689). The long description contained in Locke's travel journal is equally significant.

[17]Jaccard, *Histoire sociale du travail*, p. 185.

knowledge oriented toward the search for truth.[18] Actually, the Aristotelian conception of science itself implied a political view:

Aristotle wants to show that the Greek city, oligarchical and solidly structured along hierarchical lines, is just because it is constructed in the image of nature. Obviously, this implies that he must have begun to construct nature in the image of the city, . . . and it is by no means easy to distinguish historically what in the politics stems from the science and what in the science stems from the politics.[19]

By their polemics against the Aristotelian conception of science, their defense of the dignity of the mechanical arts,

[18]Aristotle, *Politics*, 1278a, 1319a, 1338b; cf. Plato, *Laws*, VIII; 846. On the cleavage between technics and science in the antique world: G. Glotz, *Le travail dans la Grèce ancienne* (Paris, 1920); H. Diels, *Die Antike Technik* (Leipzig, 1924) pp. 29–35, 40ff; A. Rehm "Zur Rolle der Technik in der griechisch-römischen Antike," *Archiv fur Kulturgeschichte*, vol. XXVIII (1938), pp. 135–62, is highly informative. P. M. Schuhl, *Machinisme et philosophie* (Paris, 1947), pp. 13ff. For a fundamental understanding of this whole problem, see the valuable studies by Benjamin Farrington: *Greek Science, Its Meaning for Us* (London-Baltimore, 1953), *Head and Hand in Ancient Greece* (London, 1947), *Science in Antiquity* (London, 1936), *Science and Politics in the Ancient World* (London, 1939).

M. A. Aymard, "Hierarchie du travail et autarchie individuelle dans la Grèce archaique," *Revue d'hist. de la philos. et d'hist. generale de la civilization* (1943). "L'idée du travail dans la Grèce archaique," *Journal de psychologie* (1948), has tried to show how the "contempt" for labor was absent in Greece. Despite these very numerous attempts to deny the existence of a cleavage between technics and science in the ancient world, R. J. Forbes, *Studies in Ancient Technology*, vols. I–VI (Leiden, 1955–58), whose themes were resumed in *Man the Maker* (London, 1958), and A. Koyré, "Les philosophes et la machine: les origines du machinisme," *Critique* (1948), pp. 619–29, remain fundamental achievements in this field. M. R. Cohen and I. E. Drabkim, *A Source Book in Greek Science* (New York, 1948), is an important collection of texts. L. Edelstein, "Recent Trends in the Interpretation of Ancient Science," Wiener and Noland, eds., in *Roots of Scientific Thought*, pp. 96–102, provides a broad and clear review of the state of the question.

[19]R. Lenoble, "Origines de la pensée scientifique moderne," in *Histoire de la science* (Paris, 1957), p. 391.

and rejection of the image of nature conceived as a rigid hierarchy of forms, Palissy, Vives, Agricola, and Vesalius (as later Bacon and Boyle), independently of their particular intentions and opinions or political prejudices, contributed to the destruction of a once venerated view of the world. This repudiation was not to be devoid of "political" consequences and repercussions.[20]

2.

At the same time several exponents of the current philosophical circles and not a few representatives of certain more advanced groups of artisans also made their contribution to this work of demolition—a point that merits being stressed here. These artisans, entering into relations with exponents of humanistic circles (and with the legacy of the classic world), looked for an answer to their questions in the works of Euclid, Archimedes, Vitruvius, and Hero. The literature of the fourteenth and fifteenth centuries is extraordinarily rich in treatises of a technical character, which at times were real manuals, and at times disconnected reflections on their own work or procedures employed in the various arts. Works of this type made a decisive contribution to the contact, which at that time was being effected, between scientific and technico-artisan knowledge. This had a crucial effect on the cooperation that was developing between scientists and technicians, and between science and industry. Before we proceed to an examination of some of these works and their authors, it would be opportune to recall that this literature of artists, engineers, and master craftsmen includes the writings of Brunelleschi, Ghiberti, Piero della Francesca, Leonardo, Cellini, and Paolo Lomazzo; the treatise by Konrad Keyser (1366–1405) on in-

---

[20]R. Lenoble, *Origines*, pp. 370, 376–77, 391–93. The conclusions of a general character at which Lenoble arrives merit emphasis: "Le renouveau scientifique du XVII siècle n'est en réalité qu'un aspect d'une aventure d'une tout autre ampleur, qui est une aventure humaine."

struments of warfare; the technical treatises by Fontana (1420) and those by Mariano (1438); the works on architecture by Leon Battista Alberti, Filarete, Francesco di Giorgio Martini, and Palladio; the book on military machines by Valturio da Rimini (published in 1472 and then reprinted in Verona in 1482 and 1483, in Bologna in 1483, in Venice in 1493, and four times in Paris between 1532 and 1550); the two treatises by Dürer on descriptive geometry and fortifications (1525 and 1527); Biringuccio's *Pirotechnia* (1540, later republished in two Latin, three French, and four Italian editions); the work on ballistics by Nicola Tartaglia (1537); the two treatises on mining engineering by the German, Georg Agricola (1546 and 1556); the *Teatro di macchine* by Besson (1569, later translated into French and Spanish); the *Mechanicorum libri* by Guidobaldo del Monte (1577); *Le Diverse et artificiose macchine* by Agostino Ramelli (1588); the three books on mechanics by Simon Stevin (1586, translated from the Flemish into French in 1634); the work on fortifications by Lorini (1597); and the treatises on the art of navigation by William Barlowe (1597), Thomas Harriot (1594), and Robert Hues (1599).

A renewed interest[21] in the mathematical and technical works of classical antiquity corresponded to this extremely vast production,[22] which of course is not exhausted by this brief list: the first printed edition of Euclid appeared in Venice in 1482; Francesco Maurolico (1494–1575) pub-

[21]On this literature there are several works of a general character, reserving the citation of individual authors for subsequent footnotes: A. Wolf, *A History of Science, Technology and Philosophy in the 16th and 17th Centuries* (London, 1950); the most comprehensive work in this field now is *A History of Technology*, ed. C. Singer *et al.* (Oxford, 1954–58), vols. II–III. Also useful is F. Klemm, *Technik, eine Geschichte ihrer Probleme* (Freiburg-Munich, 1954), which contains numerous texts. T. Bech, *Beitrage zur Geschichte der Maschinenbaus* (Berlin, 1900), is still the best description of these books.

[22]On the translation of the classics and their incidence, See G. Sarton, *The Appreciation of Ancient and Medieval Science during the Renaissance (1450–1600)* (Philadelphia, 1955).

lished Latin editions of Archimedes, Apollonius, and Diophantos, while Federico Commandino (1509–1575) published Euclid, Apollonius, Pappus, Hero, Archimedes, and
Aristarchus. After the beginning of the sixteenth century,
the commentaries became increasingly more organic and
broader in character, involving the addition of new notions
and often the actual completion of the text. Many translations of the classics were directed expressly to the artisans.
Jean Martin, the French translator of Vitruvius (1547),
wrote for "the workers and other people who do not understand the Latin language." Walter Rivius, presenting the
same text in German (1578), addressed himself "to the
artisans, artificers, stonecutters, architects, and weavers."[23]

The commentaries on Vitruvius, of which Vassili Zoubov[24] has made an excellent study, offer a clear example of
the importance and the significance of these "representa-
tions" of the classic texts. From that of Filander (1541) to
that of Daniel Barbaro (1556), these commentaries were
presented as real encyclopedias. Barbaro, who availed himself of Palladio's collaboration, was aware of the existence
of a considerable number of sixteenth-century texts on technics. He utilized the *Arte del navegar* by Pedro de Medino,
the treatises on proportions and the use of the compass by
Dürer, the commentaries on Ptolemy by Commandino, and
the *Compositio hologuiorum* by Sebastian Münster. Many
years before Galileo he had wanted to consult "those who
work in the Arsenal of the Venetians," and he had a keen
sense of the necessity of a fruitful union between *practice
and discourse.* "Why, therefore, have practical men not acquired credit? For the reason that architecture is born of
discourse. Why the men of letters? For the reason that

[23]W. Rivius, *Vitruvius Zehen Bücher von der Architectur und
künstilichem Bawen* . . . (Nuremburg, 1548); cf. also *Unetrichtung
zu rechten Verstand der lehr Vitruvii* (Nuremberg, 1547). Concerning German books, cf. Schlosser-Magnino, *La letteratura artistica*
(Florence, 1935), pp. 238–42.
[24]V. P. Zoubov, "Vitruve et ses commentateurs du XVIe siècle," in
La science au XVIe siècle (Paris, 1960), pp. 69–90.

architecture is born of construction. To be an architect, which is an artificial generation, one must seek discourse and construction together."[25]

3.

Despite the important investigations pursued by Leonard Olschki[26] on the "experimental masters" *(Mastri sperimentatori)* of the fifteenth century, we really know very little about how technical knowledge was passed on during that century. What is certain is that it was precisely in this century, and in Italy in particular, that the union between scientific conceptions and active life to which we have referred actually took place. Filippo Brunelleschi, the builder of the cupola of Santa Maria del Fiore (1420–1436), was an architect and sculptor, goldsmith, watchmaker, and builder of fortresses, well versed in hydraulic constructions and mechanics, and expert in the theory of proportions and perspective. After his original experience as a goldsmith, according to Vasari, it happened that "coming into contact with some studious artists, he began to study with enthusiasm motion, weights and wheels, how they may be made to revolve and what sets them in motion, and so produced with his own hand some excellent and very beautiful clocks." And it was precisely in this period, as attested by Antonio Manetti in his *Vita di Brunellesco* that "he propounded and himself practiced what the painters of today call perspective."[27] Lorenzo Ghiberti had also started out as a goldsmith. In the *Commentarii* he modeled his definition

[25]*I dieci libri dell'Architettura di Vitruvio tradotti e commentati da Monsignor Barbaro*, printed by Francesco Marcolini (Venice, 1556), p. 9.

[26]L. Olschki, *Geschichte der neusprachlichen wissenschaftlichen Literatur:* vol. I, *Die Literatur der Technik und der angewandten Wissenschaften vom Mittelalter bis zur Renaissance* (Heidelberg, 1918); vol. 2, *Bildung und Wissenschaft in Zeitalter der Renaissance in Italien* (Leipzig-Rome-Florence, 1922); vol. III, *Galilei und seine Zeit* (Halle, 1927).

[27]Cited in F. Pellati, "Vitruvio e il Brunelleschi," *La Rinascita*, vol. II (June, 1939), 7, pp. 343–65.

of the artist on that which Vitruvius had given of the architect; but to the disciplines listed by the latter he added
anatomy, optics, and theoretical and practical mathematics.[28]

It was a humanist of the stamp of Leon Battista Alberti
who launched the notion that a "scientific conception of art"
was the basis by which mathematics (i.e., theory of proportions and theory of perspective) is the common ground of
the painter and scientist: "I would like a painter to be as
learned as he can in all the liberal arts, but first I desire
that he know geometry. Our rough sketches from which is
expressed all the perfect art of painting, will be easily understood by the geometer, but he who is ignorant of geometry will not understand those nor any other method of painting: consequently I affirm that it is necessary that a painter
undertake the study of geometry."[29] Painting is a science,
and the perspective view used by painters, is also a science:
"Hence painting would be naught else but the intersection
of the visual pyramid, according to a given distance, once
the center is situated and the lighting established with lines
and colors in a certain surface artificially represented."

"Reason" and "rule," the "project" of the intelligence and
of the mind are conjoined with "action" in the work of the
architect. His task is "to bring to a conclusion all those
things which through the movements of weights, conjunc-
tions and pilings of bodies one upon the other, can with
great dignity eminently be accommodated to the uses of
men." The eulogy of the figure of the architect-engineer immediately thereafter became a eulogy to the technique
which was able to displace enormous masses of water and

[28]L. Ghiberti, *Commentarii,* ed. Schlosser (Berlin, 1912). Cf. L.
Venturi, "Lorenzo Ghiberti," *Pretesti di critica* (Milan, 1929).
[29]L. B. Alberti, *Della pittura,* ed. L. Mallé (Florence, 1950), pp.
103–04. The very important study by J. R. Spencer, "Ut rhetorica
pictura: A study in Quattrocento Theory of Painting," *Journal of
Warburg and Courtauld Institutes* (1957), pp. 26–44, is very important for an understanding of the relations between Alberti's theory of painting and the rules of oratory and rhetoric of Cicero and
Quintilianus.

rock, to drill holes into mountains and to fill valleys, to drain and reclaim swamps and divert waters, to regulate the courses of rivers, to build ships and bridges, instruments of warfare, fortresses, and, finally, to open new roads and new trade routes to all the peoples of the world.[30]

Piero della Francesca, in his *De prospectiva pingendi,* insisted upon the necessity of "science" and "geometry" along the very same lines as Alberti. "Many painters censure perspective because they do not understand the force of lines and angles that is produced by it and with which, commensurately, every contour and outline is described. Therefore, it seems to me that it is my bound duty to show how necessary this science is to painting."[31] The "censure" of many painters, to which Piero alludes, is a highly significant fact. It expresses the resistance to theory characteristic of a sensibility that was still exclusively artisan and accustomed to an artistic literature of a medieval type, namely, one composed exclusively of prescriptions. A passage from Filarete's treatise provides us with a precise and interesting testimony of this resistance.

Once I was in a place where a gentleman was dining in the company of several others, and while discussing many and sundry things they began to talk about building. One of them said: "It certainly seems as though you hold this building in great esteem. But to me it does not seem like such a great thing as so many make of it and who say, further, that it is necessary to know so many principles of geometry and drawing and many other things. Only recently I heard of one who was talking about a certain Vitruvius and of another who, it seemed, was called Archimedes who had written about this matter of building and about measurements and much other information which they say it is necessary to know. Now when I build something, I don't look for all these things and I don't bother so

[30]L. B. Alberti, *De re aedificatoria* (Florence, 1485), Preface.

[31]Piero della Francesca, *De prospectiva pingendi*, ed. G. Nicco Fasola (Florence, 1942), p. 128. On the position of Alberti, Piero, Brunelleschi, and Leonardo, cf. R. Wittkower, "Brunelleschi and 'Proportion in Perspective'," *Journal of Warburg and Courtauld Institutes* (1953), pp. 275–91.

much with all these points of geometry about which these persons speak. And yet my buildings stand up well." In response one of the others, who seemed to speak with greater gravity, said: "Don't talk like that because if you want to put up a building, I think you must have a good understanding of measurements and also of design. . . . I also believe that anyone wanting to build should also understand other elements. Therefore, you should not talk this way. I would like to talk about it not because it is my trade but only because I want to know something about it when the subject comes up. Indeed, I would pay very much to find someone who would make me understand the whys and wherefores of the measurements required to make a properly proportioned building and how and why these measures are derived. Thus I would also like to know how and why certain buildings originated." Upon hearing such a discussion I stepped forward because it pertained to my profession, there being no others in that place. . . .[32]

Actually this sensibility, and also the social position of artists, had undergone a radical change in the course of the fifteenth century. As Antal reminds us, in the fourteenth century art was still considered a manual skill. The artist was addressed with the familiar "thou" as were domestic servants. No affluent citizens and nobles would have considered the artist's status humiliating. Almost all artists of the early fifteenth century came out of artisan, peasant, and petty-bourgeois milieus. Andrea del Castagno was the son of a peasant, Paolo Uccello of a barber, and Filippo Lippi of a butcher. Pollaiuolo, as his name implies, was the son of a poultry vendor. In the early years of the century, sculptors and architects in Florence were members of the minor guild of masons and carpenters while painters were classed as associates of the major guild of doctors and druggists, together with subordinate house painters and color grinders. Indeed, apprenticeship in the ateliers began pre-

[32]Filarete, *Tractat uber die Baukunst,* ed. W. Oettingen, (Vienna, 1896), pp. 47–49. On the subject of such treatises, see L. Venturi, "La critica d'arte in Italia," *L'arte* (1917), pp. 305–26; *Storia della critica d'arte* (Florence, 1945). Bibliographical information in Schlosser-Magnino, *La letteratura italiana.*

cisely with manual chores and it was only after the apprentice had ground colors and prepared panels and canvases that he passed on to the execution of the drapings or secondary parts of the painting. As is well known, the ateliers produced not only famous paintings but insignia, flags, inlays, models for upholsterers and embroiderers, works in terra cotta, and objects wrought by goldsmiths. The goldsmith's art was common to painters and sculptors. Brunelleschi, Donatello, Ghiberti, and Ghirlandaio were all goldsmiths at first. Architects were not only building constructors, but also occupied themselves with mechanical instruments, war-engines, and the preparation of scaffolding and apparatus for festivals. "The change of ideas with respect to art" (which recently has been analyzed on a broad scale by Hauser and Antal) was linked to the increasingly profane character of artistic production, to the ever greater weight of the opinion of lay persons, as well as to the social transition of artists from the status of artisans to that of bourgeois. In Vasari's time, the mid-sixteenth century, commissions of an artisan character no longer appeared in keeping with the dignity of the artists. This was the age when Charles V stooped to pick up the brush dropped by Titian.[33] But before the figure of the artist was identified with that of the "genius," in the Florentine studios of the fifteenth century, like that of Verrochio, Ghirlandaio, and Brunelleschi, for perhaps the first time a fusion had been effected between technical and scientific activities, and manual labor and theory. Some of these studios, like Ghiberti's during the preparation of the doors to the Baptistry, were transformed into real industrial laboratories. It was in these laboratories, which were a combination of workshop and studio, and not in schools, that painters, sculptors, engineers, and technicians apprenticed. Here,

---

[33]F. Antal, *La pittura Fiorentina e il suo ambiente sociale nel Trecento e nel primo Quattrocento* (Turin, 1960), pp. 390, 391, 526; A. Hauser, *The Social History of Art* (New York, 1951), vol. I, pp. 311–14.

alongside the arts of stone-cutting and pouring bronze, as well as painting and sculpture, apprentices were taught the rudiments of anatomy, optics, calculus, perspective, and geometry, as well as the projected construction of vaults and the digging of canals. The empirical knowledge of an "unlettered man" such as Brunelleschi and Leonardo had an ambience of this kind behind it.[34] Brunelleschi, who was such an "unlettered man" ignorant of Latin and Greek, learned mathematics and geometry from Paolo Toscanelli, a great mathematician and learned man of Padua. Vasari tells us that "although Filippo was not a lettered man, he was able to argue so well from his own practice and experience that he often astonished M. Paolo."[35]

Paolo del Pozzo Toscanelli, who was admired by Cusanus and Regiomontanus for his mathematical studies, interested in optics and astrology, and in the problems of navigation and maritime transports, maker of solar watches, inspirer of Columbus, and great interpreter of Archimedes, was involved in a continuous dialogue with humanists and men of letters, and with technicians and artisans. The friendly and collaborative relations between the "engineer" Brunelleschi, the mathematician Alberti, and Toscanelli, "the new Archimedes," can truly be taken as a symbol of the process of renovation that had been set in motion in the Florentine culture of the fifteenth century.[36] This culture reached out to both the academics and men of action as well as artists, artisans, and technicians. This world was a meeting ground for scholars and men of political commitment, for practitioners of science and mechanical arts, for lovers of the

[34]On the studios ("*botteghe*"), in addition to the work cited in the previous footnote, see L. Olschki, *Renaissance in Italien*, pp. 92 and *passim;* A. Koyré, "Rapport final," *Léonardo de Vinci, et l'expérience scientifique au seizième siècle* (Paris, 1953), p. 240.

[35]Giorgio Vasari, *Lives of the Painters, Sculptors and Architects*, tr. A. B. Hinds (New York, 1966), vol. I, p. 272.

[36]E. Garin, *La cultura filosofica del Rinascimento italiano* (Florence, 1961), p. 328. On the character of Paolo Toscanelli, see pp. 313–34.

classics, and for those who were more interested in the modern world.[37]

4.

The attitude of Leonardo da Vinci, who "designed everything, rendered everything visible, and who, in written discourse, spoke as a technician addressing technicians," has been contrasted to the stately, refined Latin of Leon Battista Alberti, who "translated every structural or plastic concept into words, availing hmiself of the Latin phrase befitting the consummate humanist that he was."[38] This is a valid but limited contrast because it is meaningless in reference to certain names and because of the Florentine tendency which set humanists in opposition to artisans, seeing the two as belonging to conflicting "cultures." Leonardo, engineer and painter, technician and philosopher, has become the symbol of the victory of that sensibility which radically arrayed the liberal arts against the mechanical arts. No doubt by giving up (as Duhem wanted) the idea of making Leonardo into "a library mouse surfeit with scholasticism,"[39] we can form a sufficiently exact image of Leonardo's youthful interests which were

intimately linked to the usages of the fifteenth century, in which an education prevailed that was still artisan, manual, and mechanical . . . we see Leonardo start out from this ambience, intent not only on doing the work of painter and sculptor but also on studying, inventing, and fashioning various contrivances and instruments with a brilliance that beyond doubt was exceptional. But it was not exceptional among Florentine

[37]*Ibid.*, p. 325. For an accurate appraisal of the influence exercised by the humanistic movement on the sciences, cf. E. Garin, "Gli umanisti e la scienza," *Rivista di filosofia*, vol. III (1961), pp. 259–78.

[38]C. Maltese, "Il pensiero architettonico e urbanistico di Leonardo," in *Leonardo, saggi e ricerche per le onoranze di Leonardo da Vinci nel quinto anniversario della morte* (Rome, 1954), p. 342.

[39]R. Dugas, "Léonardo de Vinci dans l'histoire de la mécanique," in *Léonardo de Vinci et l'expérience scientifique*, p. 92.

artists to be intent on similar mechanical activities. Even his repertory—screws, springs, files, bellows, and such things— was not very far removed, at the beginning, from that which must have been common for the age and, in the last analysis, still rather rudimentary baggage of the Florentine of that time.[40]

Leonardo's awareness of the nexus that had to be established between theoretical knowledge, practical activity, and experience was born from an artisan's familiarity with the characteristics of materials and the possibilities opened up by processing them. "And if you will say that the sciences, which begin and end in the mind, are true, this is not conceded but is denied for many reasons, and first of all because no experiment occurs in such mental discourses without which nothing gives certainty of itself." Nevertheless, reciprocally, it is also true that "there is no certainty where there can be no application of one of the mathematical sciences or which are connected with these mathematics" and that "those who become enamored of practice without science are like pilots who board a ship without helm or compass, and who never are certain as to where they are going."[41] In Leonardo we see the same polemic against pure empiricists that we saw in Alberti and Filarete: "Here the adversary says that it is not science so much that he wants, and that practice suffices to draw natural things. We answer him by asserting that nothing deceives us more than to trust our judgment without any other reason, as is always proved by experiment, the enemy of alchemists, magicians and other simple minds."[42]

On this basis it is certainly possible to talk about a shifting on the part of the mature Leonardo toward theory, and to note how the complex Leonardesque projects of pumps, lock gates, and rectification and canalizations of streams of water were drawn up after the years of his sojourn in

[40]A. M. Brizzio, in *Leonardo, saggi e ricerche*, p. 278.

[41]E. Solmi, *Frammenti letterari e filosofici di Leonardo da Vinci* (Florence, 1889), pp. 84, 86; *Trattato della pittura*, p. 77.

[42]Solmi, *Trattato della pittura*, p. 739.

Milan.[43] On the other hand, it is certainly not possible, as many have attempted, to seek in the thought of this artist and eminent man of letters the foundation of experimental methods and the new science. Not unjustly, after so much insistence on the "miracle" of Leonardo, there has been a willingness to recall his utter contempt for typography and printing. Furthermore, there has been an emphasis of the fact that the evaluation that was made of the Leonardesque codexes at the time of their publication depended on the scarce or wholly nonexistent data concerning the actual situation of the scientific knowledge of the time.[44]

"In the codexes of Leonardo," writes Randall, "there is not a single scientific idea of a theoretical character that was unknown to the scientific schools organized in the Italy of that time,"[45] and an historian of the rank of George Sarton has asserted that "the development of mechanics would have been the same had Leonardo never existed."[46] These are harsh judgments. But it is difficult not to agree with Randall, Sarton, and Koyré when they point out that Leonardo's investigation, albeit full of dazzling intuitions and brilliant insights, never went beyond the level of experi-

[43]A. M. Brizio, in *Leonardo, saggi e ricerche*, p. 278.

[44]G. Sarton, "Léonardo da Vinci, ingenieur et savant," in *Léonardo da Vinci et l'expérience scientifique*, p. 19. On the positions of Leonardesque criticism on the works by Duhem: *Etudes sur Léonardo da Vinci. Ceux qu'il a lu et ceux qui l'on lu*, (Paris, 1906–1913); and on the studies by Solmi and Marcolongo: E. Solmi, "Le fonti dei manoscritti di Leonardo da Vinci, *Giornale storico della letteratura italiana*, (Süppl. nos. 10–11 [1908], pp. 1–344); "Nuovi contributi alle fonti dei manoscritti di Leonardo da Vinci," *ibid.* (1911, pp. 297–357); R. Marcolongo, "La meccanica di Leonardo da Vinci," in *Atti della R. Accademia delle scienze fisiche e naturali* (Naples, 1932). Cf. E. Garin, *La cultura filosofica del Rinascimento*, pp. 388–89. See also G. Castelfranco, "Momenti della recente critica vinciana," in *Leonardo, saggi e ricerche*, pp. 417ff. which provides a broad critical review of this field.

[45]J. H. Randall, Jr., "The Place of Leonardo da Vinci in the Emergence of Modern Science," in Wiener and Noland, eds., *Roots of Scientific Thought*, p. 209.

[46]"Intervention de M. Sarton," in *Léonardo da Vinci et l'expérience scientifique*, p. 114.

ments made for the sake of curiosity, so that it could arrive at that fundamental methodology characteristic of modern science and technology. His investigation, ever wavering between experiments and notations made out of sheer curiosity, appears fragmented, as though pulverized into a series of brief notes, scattered observations, and jottings written for himself in an obscure symbology and deliberately nontransmittible. Leonardo, who was always curious about a particular problem, actually had no interest in working on a systematic corpus of knowledge. He was alien to the concern, which indeed is a fundamental dimension of what is called technique and science, to transmit, explain, and prove his own discoveries to others.[47]

A few years after Leonardo's death, Dürer published his instructions on the use of the compass and square (1525), his study of fortifications (1527), and his work on the proportions of the human body (1528). These were published in the form of systematic treatises which could serve as useful guides to other German artists and artisans, as Leonardo's notes and jottings could not. Dürer very early had grasped the revolutionary import of the printing press and had turned his attention to the problems that had kindled Leonardo's interest.

From this point of view even the innumerable famous machines projected by Leonardo (which very probably never got beyond the project state) reacquire their real dimensions. Rather than being constructed in a spirit of progress in order to relieve the labor of men and to increase their dominion over the world and matter, they appear to have been constructed for provisional purposes: festivals, entertainments, mechanical surprises, etc. They "appear destined to play the role of marvelous instruments at jousts and spectacles." It was no accident that Leonardo was

[47]J. H. Randall, Jr., "The Place of Leonardo"; G. Sarton, "Leonardo," p. 18; E. Garin, *Medioevo e Rinascimento* (Bari, 1954), pp. 339–40. On Dürer's work, see E. Panofsky, *The Life and Art of A. Dürer* (Princeton, 1955).

more concerned with the elaboration rather than the execution of his projects; he was interested in machines more as the result and proof of human intelligence and genius than as a means for the actual mastery of nature.[48] Machines risked becoming toys for the entertainment of sovereigns, while the concept of force on which there had been so much insistence was certainly linked more to the Hermetic and Ficinian theme of universal animation than to rational mechanics. "Force is a spiritual, incorporeal, and impalpable spiritual potency . . . because there is an invisible, incorporeal, and impalpable life in it. . . . Force is naught else but a spiritual virtue, an invisible potency which is created and infused, through accidental violence, by sensible into insensible bodies, giving to these bodies the similitude of life."[49]

Rather than relate back to the so-called philosophical themes of Leonardo's thought, in which widely diffused motives are repeated, or to his physics with its vague and inconstant terminology, it would be more useful to refer to his observations on vision and painting and to his desire "to render all visible" which we noted at the beginning. In the designs of machines, as in his anatomical drawings, Leonardo truly made a decisive contribution to the invention of a precise method for the representation and description of reality. Here generic empiricism became experimentalism; experiment made way for active and operative investigation. Nor must we forget that the invention of that method of rigorous description of natural reality, which was the work of the great artists of the fifteenth century, has the

[48]For this appraisal of Leonardo's machines see E. Garin, *Medioevo e Rinascimento,* p. 337; E. Wind, "Leonardo da Vinci: Mathematics and Sensibility," *The Listener* (May 1, 1952); A. Chastel, "Léonardo et la culture," in *Léonardo da Vinci et l'expérience scientifique,* p. 263. For a different appraisal see A. Koyré, "Rapport final," *ibid.,* p. 242; C. Luporini, *La mente di Leonardo* (Florence, 1953); V. Somenzi, "Ricostruzione deue macchine per il volo; Leonardo e i principi della dinamica," in *Leonardo, saggi e ricerche,* pp. 59ff., 147ff.

[49]E. Garin, *Medioevo e Rinascimento,* pp. 331–33.

same importance for the descriptive sciences (as Erwin Panofsky has pointed out) as did the invention of the telescope or of the microscope in the seventeenth century.[50] To convince ourselves of this, we need merely think of Dürer's etchings or of the anatomical charts of Vesalius' work that came out of Titian's school. Leonardo had an extremely keen sense of this power of figuration and was fully aware of the revolutionary import of this attitude. Linked to it is his thesis of the superiority of the eye to the mind, and of the direct and detailed observation of the real world to books and writings. It was precisely in reference to painting that Leonardo turned back to confront a theme that was being widely discussed in the culture of his time: "You [writers] have placed painting among the mechanical arts; to be sure, if painters were as capable of praising their work in writing as you are, I doubt that it would be under so base a designation. If you call it mechanical, because it is first manual in that the hands draw what they had in the imagination, you writers manually design with the pen what is found in your mind."

5.

In reality, Leonardo's polemic, like that of many other artists of the fifteenth century, did not intend to overcome the age-old opposition between the mechanical and liberal arts. Rather, it tended to justify the insertion of painting and sculpture within the list of the so-called liberal arts. The problem has been formulated with great clarity by Cesare Luporini. With the new appraisal of the figure of the artist, he asks, and with the glory that surrounded him in Italy from the beginning of the fifteenth century on, "was it the entire world in which he had his roots [namely, the world of manual and artisan activities] that was raised in the new social valuation of the artist, or was he rather

[50]F. S. Bodenheimer, "Towards the History of Zoology and Botany in the XVIth Century," in *La science au seizième siècle*, p. 288.

detached from it in order to pass on to a higher sphere?" There is no doubt about the answer. By passing from the status of artisan to that of bourgeois, artists were detached from the "studios" and absorbed into a culture that was higher on the social scale and linked to the courts and the "service" of princes. "Lorenzo the Magnificent's creation of the garden of St. Mark, the cultivation in it of young artistic geniuses taken from the studios, is an event to which we must attribute a symbolic value."[51]

The process that led to a new, different evaluation of the mechanical arts and of the work of technicians, and that led to the recognition of the function exercised by artisans and engineers within the culture and society, exhibited very different characteristics. For one thing it had a European character and was linked to the rise of the bourgeoisie, and to the consolidation of the monarchies and nation-states. But what must be stressed here is that this new evaluation, which was the product of a new historical reality, made

[51]C. Luporini, *La mente di Leonardo*, p. 136. In this connection we should also recall the polemics, widespread in the sixteenth century, over the "dignity" of architecture and over the comparison between architecture and painting. The thesis that maintains architecture superior to painting is linked to the prominence given the "mathematical" foundations of the former and the "manual" character of the latter. A position of this type is present in J. Sute, *The First and Chief Groundes of Architecture* (London, 1563) and in the Preface by J. Dee to the translation of Euclid's *Élements* (London, 1570). On this subject see the important article by L. Salerno, "Seventeenth-Century English Literature on Painting," *Journal of Warburg and Courtauld Institutes*, vol. XIV (1951), pp. 234–58. Here we also see how in the controversy over architecture between Inigo Jones and Ben Jonson the former defends architecture and considers manual labor wholly secondary, where the latter identifies the figure of the architect with that of an artisan and ridicules Vitruvian architecture's claim to being scientific and universal. On this polemic, see D. J. Gordon, "Poet and Architect: The Intellectual Setting of the Quarrel between Ben Jonson and Inigo Jones," *Journal of Warburg and Courtauld Institutes*, vol. XII (1949), pp. 152ff. The theme of the "dependence upon geometry" of many crafts and of many sectors of natural philosophy also requires a more thorough treatment. On this subject, see the discussion (led by E. Panofsky, *The Life and Art of A. Dürer*, pp. 161ff.) on the image of geometry present in *Margarita Philosophica* by Reisch, and *Melancolia* by Dürer.

possible that collaboration between scientists and technicians and that copenetration of technology and science which was at the root of the great scientific revolution of the seventeenth century. The direction of the scientific movement was to pass on to the engineers, to the *virtuosi*, and to the gentlemen "of scientific spirit" of the seventeenth century. The organs of the new culture were no longer to be the universities, but the scientific societies and the academies. The scientific method was not to be the end in itself which the early experimental investigations had limited themselves to "illustrate": instead "proof of practice" was to have a decisive effect also on the elaboration of theories of the most general character.[52]

We must dwell precisely on these concepts if we are to grasp the profound distance that separates medieval science from the modern science and the truly revolutionary character of the latter. There is no doubt that the traditional images of a medieval "night" and of a Renaissance which victoriously and forever scattered its shadows have now been discarded. We cannot deny the spirit of invention and observation, as was once fashionable, to the epoch which produced the great Roman basilicas and the great Gothic cathedrals, which invented or reinvented, adapted, or inserted into our civilization the attaching of horses, shoeing, the stirrup, the water mill, windmill, plane, winder, compass, gun powder, and which saw the appearance of spectacles, mechanical clocks, and the scale.[53] Once all this has been clarified, it nevertheless remains perfectly true (as is recognized by A. Crombie, an eminent student of medieval scientific thought, who has strongly emphasized the elements of continuity between medieval and modern science) that the greater part of the technical progress of the Middle Ages was probably the work of illiterate artisans. The "di-

[52]A. Crombie, *Histoire des sciences de Saint Augustin à Galilée* (Paris, 1959), p. 318.

[53]L. Febvre, *Le problème de l'incroyance au XVI siècle* (Paris, 1946), pp. 412ff. See also A. Koyré, "Du monde de l'a peu près à l'univers de la précision," *Critique* (1948), p. 809.

rection of the interest" of medieval physicists "could have turned out to be fatal for the science of the West" for the reason that "they never submitted their methods to the test of practice,"[54] despite the excellence of their methodology. Alexandre Koyré rightly considers the developments of medieval technics as a striking proof of the autonomous possibilities of development of a *techné* that moves on the plane of common sense:

The technical thought of common sense does not depend on the scientific thought of which it can nevertheless absorb the elements, incorporating them into common sense; it can develop, invent, adapt ancient discoveries to new needs and even make new discoveries; guided and prodded by experience and action, successes and failures, it can transform the rules of *techné;* it can also create and develop tools and machines. Indeed, with means that are often rudimentary, it can, served by the skill of those who use them, create works whose perfection (not to mention beauty) by far surpasses the product of scientific technics, especially when the latter was in its beginnings.[55]

Even if we do not accept all the implications present in Koyré's overly rigid distinction, it nevertheless is beyond doubt that in a cultural situation of this type, the technico-scientific relation in its general lines shapes up more like an act of divorce than one of collaboration. On this point Erwin Panofsky, in his discussion of medieval treatises on the arts (architecture, mechanical engineering, metal, processing, etc.), has arrived at very precise results: between the writings of Theophilus, Villard de Honnecourt, Jean de la Bégue, and Martin Roriczer and those of Leon Battista Alberti, Piero della Francesca, and Georgio Martini, there exists the same difference as between a collection of pharmaceutical recipes and a work on biochemistry. The medieval technical writings gave ample and detailed instructions on the way "to work." They offered themselves as a

---

[54]A. Crombie, *Histoire des sciences*, pp. 154, 317–18.
[55]A. Koyré, "Du monde de l'a peu près à l'univers," p. 809.

compilation of rules, recipes, and precepts. They were completely devoid of "theory" understood as an attempt to derive the precepts from general principles and then to base them on a totality of verifiable facts.

A medieval treatise on architecture, for instance, whether covering the whole field or concentrating on a special problem, shows only what things can be done and how they should be done; it makes no attempt to explain to the reader why they have to be done in this peculiar way, let alone to supply him with a system of general concepts on the basis of which he may cope with problems not yet foreseen by the writer. The reader is given praiseworthy examples of ground plans, elevations, structural details, ornaments, etc., partly selected from existing monuments and partly invented by the author himself; he is informed about the right way of joining the stones; . . . he is taught such indispensable methods of geometrical drawing as parallel projection, . . . the construction of regular polygons, etc.; but he is not given a "theory of architecture."

This was precisely what a writer like Leon Battista Alberti proposed to do. Basing himself on Vitruvius, but varying, expanding and even correcting him in all directions, he derives his prescriptions from general principles such as practical purpose, convenience, order, symmetry and optical appearance. He divides the tasks of the architecture in different classes which, taken together, form a coherent and comprehensive system from city planning to the construction of fireplaces, and he tries to corroborate his statements both by deductive, though naturally not always critical, reasoning and by historical evidence.[56]

Here Panofsky is referring to the technicians and artisans insofar as they are writers of treatises, whether precepts or real "theories." In a discussion of the actual work of architects insofar as they were builders, Pierre Francastel has arrived at identical conclusions relative to the problem that interests us here. In the construction of the cupola of Santa Maria del Fiore, Brunelleschi abandoned the medieval system of wooden scaffolding supporting the temporary frames on which the vaulted work was constructed, and which at

[56]E. Panofsky, *The Life and Art of A. Dürer*, pp. 242–43.

the same time served as the section of a design, framework, and provisional supports. Brunelleschi understood, before actually effecting it, "that it was possible to build the dual spheroidal vault of the cupola working in the void, without the temporary frames for sustaining the light materials during the actual operations and the setting of the mortar." This presupposed two things: "an admirable artisan expertise [the circular laying of the elements followed a design which did not enable the worker to see the final form] and the capacity to prearrange the development of the work in terms of an abstract view of the forms." The traditional empirical procedures had to be discarded. It was no longer a question of

reckoning from the ground, on the basis of the stones whose outline is deduced from that of the adjoining one and which can be rigorously tested on the scaffold. Now it was necessary to determine with abstract calculation the inclination and the laying of multiple and small elements such as the bricks in particular in terms of a twofold purpose [armature and filling] without any possibility of correction or checking.

With Brunelleschi, architecture "passed from a phase of empirical technicism to a mathematical speculation. The builder of the Renaissance was an intellectual, his counterpart in the Middle Ages was an artisan."[57]

It should be stressed that this is not merely a matter of conclusions elaborated by art historians of the Renaissance. The extremely minute analysis that John F. Fichten[58] has

[57]P. Francastel, *Lo spazio figurativo dal Rinascimento al Cubismo* (Turin, 1957), pp. 95, 204, 206–07. On Brunelleschi, see the important study by G. C. Argan, "The Architecture of Brunelleschi and the Origins of Perspective Theory in the Fifteenth Century," *Journal of Warburg and Courtauld Institutes* (1946), to which Francastel refers several times. See also R. Wittkower, *Principles of Architecture in the Time of Humanism* (London, 1950).

[58]J. F. Fichten, 3d, *The Construction of Gothic Cathedrals* (Oxford, 1961); see also P. Frankl, "The Secret of Medieval Masons," *Art Bulletin* (1942).

made of the methods employed by the builders of Gothic cathedrals confirms the correctness of these conclusions: the creators of those admirable masterpieces moved on a plane of artisan empiricism which always remained at the level of practice.

If an investigation were conducted into the different areas, It would most probably yield very similar results. It is certain, however, that the collaboration between technical and scientific knowledge that was ushered in at the beginning of modern times is to be considered as one of the central and fundamental aspects of the new culture. This collaboration, not accidentally, played a crucial role with respect to the utilization that was made on a scientific plane of not a few devices and techniques already known to medieval civilization. For example, more variants were designed of the astrolabe, the most characteristic of all the scientific instruments of the Middle Ages, during the last half of the century of its use in Europe (1575–1625) than in all previous history. Lenses were already known in the thirteenth century, and perhaps at the end of the twelfth. For three centuries, a kind of conspiracy of silence was entered into concerning them. Cognizance was taken of them and they became an object of theoretical study only in the sixteenth century in the writings of Francesco Maurolico (which, however, were ignored until 1611) and in the *Magia naturalis* by Giambattista della Porta (1589). Kepler was to lay the foundation of the new optics in the *Paralipomena of* 1604, but it was to be a scientist-technician like Galileo who was to muster up the courage "to look" by using the telescope. He skillfully transformed a use-object which had progressed only "through practice," partly accepted in military circles but ignored by the official scientific establishment, into a powerful instrument of scientific exploration.[59]

[59]See V. Ronchi, *Galileo e il canocchiale* (Udine, 1942); "L'optique au XVIe siècle," in *La science au XVIe siècle*, pp. 49–62.

Mechanical clocks, one of the greatest technical inventions of the Middle Ages, go back to the thirteenth century. In many instances they were very beautiful and complicated mechanisms which could reproduce the celestial movements, set a procession of figures in motion, and strike the hours with chimes. But their precision, clearly inferior to that of the water clocks of antiquity, appeared as an inadequacy even within the frame of medieval society where the typical peasant custom of disregard for the exact time was very much alive. Up to the first half of the sixteenth century, time was still "lived time"—that common sense conception of time by which life flows on according to the natural measurements of day and night or of the motions of the celestial vault. Only in the second half of the sixteenth century, hand in hand with the growth of urban wealth and the victory of urban life over peasant life, was there a felt need for a more exact measurement of time. The widespread use of the clock along with the construction of even more precise mechanisms goes back to this period. In this case, the precision clock, the clock conceived not simply as a use-object but as a scientific instrument, was born at that moment when the contact between technics and science arrived at its full maturation in the work of Galileo (1582) and Huygens (1657). The demand for exact time measurement, for which traditional watches had proved wholly inadequate, derived from the "internal" requirements of astronomy and physics. This same demand also derived from the needs of ocean navigation and from the problems linked to the determination of the "point":

Latitude is easily determinable through observation of the sun or of the polar star; the determination of longitude requires knowledge of the hour of a meridian-base of origin. This hour must be taken along, it has to be preserved, and it is necessary to have a trustworthy custodian of time. The two problems of the measurement and of the conservation of time were closely bound up with each other. The former was solved by Huygens and Galileo who utilized the pendulum for this purpose. The latter was solved perfectly, at least in principle, thanks to Huygens' invention of the gimbal-spiral system.[60]

We could easily multiply examples of this kind. Indeed, from many quarters there had been an expected insistence on the importance that many practical problems (such as those of the speed of ships, of the construction of canals, ballistics, the manufacture of pumps, the ventilation of mines) assumed with respect to the birth and the progress of a series of investigations of a theoretical character (hydrostatics, hydrodynamics, chronometry, and dynamics). The re-evaluation of technical knowledge and the new social prestige acquired by artisans and engineers was further closely bound up with the increased economic importance of some sectors of the traditional mechanical arts (for example, metallurgy, mining, and navigation). Nor can the weighty role played in this profound change by the development of the great voyages of exploration, maritime routes, mercantile capital, and of the mining industry ever be sufficiently stressed.[61]

In more than one sector the collaboration between the

[60]A. Jacquerod's Preface to L. Défossez, *Les savants du XVIIe siècle et la mesure du temps* (Lausanne, 1946). For the methods employed in the determination of longitude, see A. Mackay, *The Theory and Practice of finding the Longitude at Sea or Land* (London, 1812), vol. II, pp. 217–18; R. K. Merton, "Science, Technology and Society in Seventeenth-Century England," *Osiris*, vol. IV (1938), pp. 526–33. On clocks and time, see W. L. Milham, *Time and Timekeepers* (New York, 1945); A. Koyré, "Les philosophes et la machine: les origines du machinisme," *Critique* (1948), pp. 626–27 and, "Du monde de l'à peu près à l'univers," pp. 806–23; A. Lloyd, "Mechanical Timekeepers," in Singer *et al.*, eds., *A History of Technology*, pp. 648–75. Information of a general character can be found in L. C. Bolton, *Time Measurement* (London, 1924); M. Daumas, *Les instruments scientifiques, aux XVIIe et XVIIIe siècles* (Paris, 1953).

[61]In addition to the general works already cited, see J. V. Neff, *La naissance de la civilisation industrielle* (Paris), pp. 35–82; A. R. Hall, *The Scientific Revolution* (London, 1954), pp. 217–24; the chapter "The Economic Incentives to Inventions," in G. N. Clark, *Science and Social Welfare in the Age of Newton* (Oxford, 1937).

"master craftsmen" and scientists turned out to be a matter of necessity, not only in connection with ballistics, architecture, and construction of fortifications, but also in the case of surgeons who were entering into ever closer contact with artists, doctors, and anatomists, builders of nautical and musical instruments, navigators linked to the investigations of mathematicians, astronomers, and cosmographers. In the face of a growing demand, the manufacture of precision instruments became a veritable industry after the middle of the sixteenth century.[62] Artisans were not only in the pay of a sovereign or of a rich patron but had a larger clientele and several workshops. For example, the Arsenius brothers in Louvain; Coignet in Antwerp; Cole, Digges, and Gemini in England—all achieved wide fame. An intense and continuous migration of artisans and technicians which lasted for many years was set in motion in different European countries. Louis XI (1461–1483) asked for German glaziers and printers, for Italian and Spanish military engineers. Rulers in Cologne and Marseilles, as well as the Duke of Brittany, extended invitations to Italian silk weavers between 1470 and 1480. Genoese and Neapolitan engineers worked for Francis I; the architect Fioravanti taught the method of "pouring" metal for the construction of cannon in Moscow; the Czars turned to Danish printers and German metallurgists (1550 and 1556), and the Italian heretic Giacomo Aconcio, to cite one name among many, obtained a contract in 1563 to drain the land flooded by the Thames and became a member of a commission of experts sent by Elizabeth I to prepare fortifications on the border with Scotland.

Cartography, which aimed at providing even more precise instruments, notably flourished in this period. The treatise on the cartographic methods by Apianus (Peter

[62]On the industry of precision instruments, in addition to Daumas, *Les instruments scientifiques*, see *Histoire de la science*, pp. 139–44; D. J. Price, "Precision Instruments to 1500; The Manufacture of Scientific Instruments from 1500 to 1700," in Singer *et al.*, eds., *History of Technology*, pp. 582–647.

Bennewitz) dates from 1524; the method of triangulation devised by Frisius harks back to 1533; that of Mercator to 1569. Of particular significance, however, was the situation concerning the relations between mathematics and astronomy with the art of navigation. The Casa de Contratación, the great school of navigation in Seville (founded in 1503), was not in any sense an isolated case. After the middle of the century a group of English mathematicians expressly set out to improve the mathematical instruction of master craftsmen, dedicating themselves at the same time to the teaching of new "scientific" methods of ocean navigation. The mathematicians Robert Recorde (1510–1558) and John Dee (1527–1606) were technical consultants of the Muscovy Company and that of Cathay. John Dee instructed and advised the most famous voyagers of the Elizabethan age), from Martin Frobisher to Sir Humphrey Gilbert, from John Davis to Sir Walter Raleigh. He not only placed a vast library at the disposal of his pupils and disciples, a library which in 1583 included more than four thousand volumes, but also his large collection of scientific instruments. Thomas Digges, another celebrated mathematician and astronomer, went to sea for several months to demonstrate some new methods. For his part, Thomas Harriot accompanied Sir Walter Raleigh's colonists to Virginia in 1585 as "practical mathematician" and scientific adviser.[63]

In 1597 the Company of Mercers, the Mayor and the Elders of London, using funds left as a legacy by Sir Thomas Gresham (1519–1579), founded the celebrated Gresham College, the most impressive English scientific center of the first half of the seventeenth century. Gresham's testament had stipulated that three of the seven academic chairs were to be in scientific subjects and explicitly prescribed that the professor of astronomy was also to teach the art of navigation. Henry Briggs (1561–1630), the first professor of geometry at the College, was a member of the

[63]E. G. R. Taylor, *Tudor Geography* (London, 1930), pp. 24–27, and *Late and Early Stuart Geography* (London, 1943), pp. 29–30.

Virginia Company. He and his colleagues, professors of mathematics and astronomy, had close links with an important group of shipbuilders and navigators.[64]

The ballad "in honor of the elect company of philosophers and subtle minds who meet on the Wednesday of every week at Gresham College" was probably written by Joseph Glanvill:

> This college will the whole world measure
> Which most impossible conclude,
> And navigation make a pleasure
> By finding out the longitude!
> Every Tarpaulian shall then with ease
> Saile any ship to the Antipodes.[65]

There is no doubt that *De magnete* by William Gilbert, published in 1600, is a fundamental work of modern science. At times certain external data are indicative of a real situation more than any well-articulated discourse. As Edgar Zilsel has pointed out, a tenth part of *De magnete* is devoted to cosmology, a little more than half the work deals with magnetism, another tenth discusses the extraction, fusion, and the processing of iron, and an entire fourth of the book is concerned with problems of navigation and nautical instruments.[66] Gilbert was thoroughly knowledgeable about the techniques of fusing metals and of mining engineering and was also greatly interested in the practical problems of ocean navigation. He had greatly utilized the work of the "master craftsmen" of his time. In particular, he had availed himself of the studies and observations of Robert Norman, "expert mariner and ingenious artisan,"

[64]F. R. Johnson, "The Gresham College: Precursors of the Royal Society," in Wiener and Noland, eds., *Roots of Scientific Thought,* pp. 328–53; J. Ward, *The Life of the Gresham Professors* (London, 1740), p. 19.

[65]See D. Stimson, "Ballad of Gresham College," *Isis,* XVIII (1932), pp. 103–17.

[66]E. Zilsel, "The Origins of Gilbert's Scientific Method," in Wiener and Noland, eds., *Roots of Scientific Thought,* pp. 230–31.

and of the work carried out by William Borough, former commander of a British ship in the battle with the Armada, and author of *A Discourse of the Variation of the Compas, or Magneticall Needle*.[67]

We find Norman's name listed on a significant roster of artisans who had been formed outside the universities and the official culture. Gabriel Harvey, a follower of Machiavelli and keenly interested in every cultural novelty, was clearly aware of the importance that the advent of this new culture of the *indocti* was assuming.

Whoever remembers the mathematician-mechanic Humphrey Cole, the shipbuilder Mathew Baker, the architect John Sute, the navigator Robert Norman, the artillerist William Bourne, the chemist John Hester or other similar sagacious and subtle empiricists, must be a very haughty man if he despises artisan experts or any sensible and industrious practical man, no matter how unlectured in schools or unlettered in books.[68]

6.

The books on machines published in Europe between the middle of the sixteenth century and the middle of the seventeenth century were the products of this situation, and all, without exception, were directed toward the search for solutions to the new problems posed by the very rapid developments in the arts, mining, warfare, metallurgy, and navigation. They were conceived and written in a cultural climate in which great changes and great geographical and astronomical discoveries were taking place. These books contained not only descriptions of existing machines, but more often projects (at times impossible to carry out) of new machines to be constructed.

[67] W. Borough, *A Discourse of the Variation of the Compas, or Magneticall Needle*, which is included in all the editions of Norman's work (see footnote 8 above).

[68] G. Harvey, *Works*, ed. A. B. Grosart (London, 1884–1885), vol. II, p. 289. On the English artisans of the sixteenth century see F. R. Johnson, "Preparation and Innovation in the Progress of Science," *Journal of the History of Ideas*, I (1943).

This observation leads us to stress one final point: the recognition that the mechanical arts presented a real interest for the development of science. There was also a new awareness of the methodological presuppositions which were at the base of technical work. These changes contributed greatly to strengthening the concept that a theory must in some way be "applied to the facts" if it was to be considered correct or confirmed. For many, a closer study and observation of the mechanical arts than had been customary in the past brought in its wake an awareness of the separation existing in the traditional culture between *globus mundi*, that is, between the conceptual structure of the sciences (their so-called theoretical apparatus) and their concrete capacity to serve human purposes by taking account of new facts. In these centuries there was continuous discussion, with an insistence that bordered on monotony, about a logic of invention conceived as a *venatio*, a hunt—as an attempt to penetrate territories never known or explored before. This logic of invention was itself viewed as an instrument; it seemed comparable, and in fact *was* often compared, to tools. It was scarcely interested in the analysis of the terms of discourse, and almost always had a tone of crudeness and naïveté if compared with the subtle discussions of late Scholasticism. In contrast to Scholasticism, it seemed above all concerned with projecting new methods and with extending the possibility of man's dominion over other men and over nature. The prodigious extension of the frontiers of the celestial and terrestrial world which took place in the sixteenth century did not fail to find an echo in the works of the philosophers and the logicians, or in the works of master craftsmen and technicians.

We find only a faint echo of these discussions and problems in considering those books on mining technique, machine construction, architecture, hydraulics, and fortifications building, which formed a large part of the publications produced in the late sixteenth century. Certainly it would be futile to look for a full awareness of the radical changes which this grandiose development also brought into the spheres of philosophy and culture in the words of Biringuccio and Agricola on metals, Vittorio Zonca on machines, or of Giacomo Strada on windmills which appeared at the beginning of the seventeenth century. Nevertheless, in some of these works there is no absence of attitudes that have a precise and prominent cultural feature.

Vannuccio Biringuccio's book on *Pirotechnia* was published in Venice in 1540.[69] This was the first printed book dealing with metallurgy, and as Farrington writes, "Its author was aware of its originality. He boasted of his uniqueness in publishing a book that was not based on other books but was drawn from the direct experience of nature."[70] Farrington's assertion concedes perhaps too much to Biringuccio's originality, but the fact remains that the author of *Pirotechnia* arrived at the point where he explicitly theorized about the function the investigation of new facts can exercise with a view to the enlargement of human knowledge. These *"notitie nuove,"* as Biringuccio called them, have the task of inspiring new inventions and the progressive broadening of our factual knowledge. They are the "keys to bring about the reawakening of minds," and without their foundation there can be no hope of being able to arrive at the goals that are proposed to us. The work's inten-

[69]V. Biringuccio, *De la pirotechnica libri dieci dove ampiamente si tratta non solo di ogni sorte e diversità di miniere, ma ancora quanto si ricerca intorno alla practica di quelle cose di quel che si appartiene a l'arte de la fusione over gitto de metalli cone d'ogni altra cosa simile a questa* (Venice, 1540). The work was reprinted in Venice in 1550, 1558, 1559, and 1687. A French translation appeared in Paris in 1556 and again in 1572. A Latin translation was published in Cologne in 1658. The citations that follow in the text are taken from *The Pirotechnia of Vanuccio Biringuccio, Ten Books in which Are Fully Treated not only Every Kind and Sort of Mineral but also All that Is Necessary for the Practice of Those Things Belonging to the Arts of Smelting or Casting Metals and All Related Subjects, Composed by Signor Vannuccio Biringuccio of Siena,* tr. Cyril Stanley Smith and Martha Teach Gnudi (New York, 1942).

[70]B. Farrington, *Francis Bacon, Philosopher of Industrial Science* (New York, 1963).

tion was descriptive; Biringuccio rejected all manner of rhetorical embellishment in the name of a faithful and stylistically bare description. He viewed rhetorical flourishes only as a device employed by men who, wanting "to show that they are masters, adorn their words when speaking of things in order to color their lies better with a thousand fables.[71]

He placed the alchemists in this category, and the polemic he conducted against the claims of alchemy is based on what he points to as the nontechnical and noncodifiable character of the processes employed by its practitioners. "All those men," writes Biringuccio, "who want to lead things to a certain end must needs think of the means required to lead them thereto." The alchemists evidently rejected this methodological precept and operated without taking it into account. Moreover, being avid for immediate, practical results, they neglected every patient investigation of the means: "The great desire that they have to become rich causes them to gaze in the distance and hinders them from seeing the intermediate steps because they are thinking only of the final result."[72]

In the face of a series of successive failures, according to Biringuccio, alchemists made no attempt to modify or perfect their techniques; rather, they invoked chance, or the intervention of accidental forces, or their incomprehension of the signified "recesses." "How many alchemists have I heard lamenting, one because by some unfortunate chance he had spilled his whole composition in the ashes; another because he had been deceived by the excessive strength of the fire, so that the substance of his materials had been burned and the spirits inadvertently allowed to escape; and yet another because he had poor and feeble materials!"[73] According to Biringuccio the insistent appeal to (often imaginary) authorities by which the alchemists deluded

[71]V. Biringuccio, *Pirotechnia*, p. 425.
[72]*Ibid.*, p. 39.
[73]*Ibid.*, p. 41.

themselves that they could eliminate the demand for rational explanations (causes) and results (effects) that could be checked is in keeping with their characteristic absence of method. The alchemists adduced more "authorities" than "witnesses."

But many are quoted by the credulous, who advance the authority of hearsay in place of reasons for possible success or facts that can be demonstrated. Among others they cite Hermes, Arnold, Raymond, Geber, Occam, Craterrus, the holy Thomas, Pariginus, and a Brother Elias of the order of St. Francis—which one I don't know. To these because of the dignity of their philosophical training or because of their holiness, the credulous demand that a certain respect be accorded through faith, so that whoever listens either is silent through ignorance or confirms what they say. But it is not this way that such men persuade those who have good judgment that the art of alchemy is true.[74]

Biringuccio's polemic against alchemy is certainly not reducible (as some have attempted—especially Thorndike)[75] to a kind of simple skepticism regarding the possibility of a transmutation of metals. He sketched the lines of an interpretation of the procedures employed in alchemy, and he understood the difference between the procedures of "magic" and those of "technical knowledge." He pointed out the futility of a work that was incapable of arriving at a codification of "means" as well as the uselessness of an appeal to tradition which could not take the place of theoretical investigations or the achievement of actual results. Nevertheless, it would be erroneous to recognize in Biringuccio's assertions the expression of a "modern" mentality. The ultimate reasons for his rejection of alchemy and for his definition of it as a "vain wish" and "fanciful dream" derived from his conviction, which had clear and distinct

[74]*Ibid.*, p. 36.
[75]L. Thorndike, *A History of Magic and Experimental Science* (New York, 1951), vol. V, p. 544: "The opening chapter is skeptical as to the possibility of transmutation."

medieval origins, that "*art* is very weak" with respect to nature and that it ends up as an attempt to imitate nature's work, Biringuccio writes:

. . . Finally taking all the alchemist principles and comparing them with the processes of nature and pondering on the procedures of the one and of the other, it seems to me that there is no proportion between their powers, granting that nature operates in things from within and causes all of her basic substances to pass wholly one into the other, while art, very weak in comparison, follows nature in an effort to imitate her, but operates in external and superficial ways.[76]

The polemic against the magico-alchemist tradition acquired a wholly different significance when it appeared in Bacon and Descartes based on the identity between the products of art and those of nature: the "paths of art" were not to appear external and superficial, nor was the attempt to transform natural reality through a knowledge of its behavior and its laws any more to appear doomed to failure.

If from Biringuccio's *Pirotechnia* we now proceed to the works of Agricola,[77] we find repeated some of the themes on which Biringuccio had already dwelt. In contrast to him, Agricola (Georg Bauer) was a man of vast culture and

[76]V. Biringuccio, *Pirotechnia*, p. 37: "I know that alchemists become angry with those who speak in derogatory fashion of their art. . . . I am content to have done this with so little offense because, in order to show my ignorance to the world, the desire may come to some worthy philosopher and alchemist to bring to light at least the open arguments for their art." P. 43. For a broader discussion of the art-nature relationship, see ch. 4 below.

[77]Agricola's works were published in Basle in the years indicated in the text and went through numerous printings. The critical edition is G. Agricola, *Ausgewählte Werke* (Berlin, 1955–1958): Band I, *G. Agricola und seine Zeit*, ed. H. Wiesdorf; Band II, *Bermannus oder über den Bergbau;* Band III, *Schriften zur Mineralogie und Geologie, I;* Band IV, *Schriften zur mineralogie und Geologie, II.* On Agricola and on the developments of the art of mining and metallurgy, see B. Dibner, *Agricola on Metals* (Norwalk, 1958).

The citations to follow in the text are taken from Herbert Clark Hoover and Lou Henry Hoover, *Giorgius Agricola, De re metallica* (New York, 1950).

broad interests. He was born in Glauchau (Saxony) in 1494, and studied at Leipzig, Bologna, and Venice. In 1527 he had begun the practice of medicine at Joachimstal in Bohemia, at that time the greatest mining region in Europe. During his lifetime Agricola enjoyed the esteem of Erasmus, Fabricius, and Melanchthon; he was also *burgermeister* of Chemnitz and was entrusted with various political missions at the courts of Emperor Charles and King Ferdinand of Austria. *De ortu et causis subterraneorum* and *De natura fossilium*, both published in 1546, were the first systematic treatments of geology and mineralogy. *De re metallica*, published in 1556, one year after the death of its author, remained for two centuries the fundamental and unsurpassed work on mining technology. The books had appeared in the same years when the prodigious mines of Central and South America were in a state of development. In Potosi, which now furnished gold and silver to all Europe, Agricola's work was considered a kind of bible, and the priests placed *De re metallica* on the altars of the churches so that the miners would come to perform their devotions every time they had a technical problem to solve.[78]

In Agricola's work one discerns first of all an awareness of a deep cultural crisis characterized by the age-old lack of interest in the "study of things" and in the observation of natural phenomena. There was also apparent a process of slow degeneration of scientific language in which the terminological clarity of the classic epoch is replaced by a linguistic barbarism which no longer makes for easy communication. Agricola tells us that the use of "strange" names has "nearly clouded over all the arts, . . . and already a common death and disintegration of all of them was approaching, if divine providence did not remedy the situation." This aspect of the decadence of the natural sciences had been remedied, according to Agricola, by the reflowering of classic Latin in Italy and the rebirth of eloquence

[78]J. V. Nef, *La naissance de la civilisation industrielle*, p. 115.

through the work of the humanists. The situation with respect to the first point struck him as being particularly serious:

The knowledge of things that is so broad, indeed that it embraces all that which can be understood with the feelings and the mind, to a great measure is still held in contempt. For, leaving aside mentioning many other things, many are the things—in particular species of animals, of plants, and of other things which the earth generates in herself—which are wholly hidden and unknown.[79]

What Agricola proposed to defend and revive was the study of natural objects, because it is through the study of nature that man can arrive at nobler and loftier goals that seemingly nature herself had assigned to his species.[80] In the preface to *De re metallica* he made clear how his work originated from an attitude of scrupulous diligence:

I have devoted much labor and care, and have even gone to some expense upon it; for with regard to the veins, tools, vessels, sluices, machines, and furnaces, I have not only described them, but have also hired illustrators to delineate their forms, lest descriptions which are conveyed by words should either not be understood by the men of our times, or should cause difficulty to posterity.[81]

The attitude assumed here by Agricola compares closely with that adopted twenty years before by Vesalius in a different field of research. Both affirmed the conviction that the condition of a particular field of knowledge required vast preparatory work of observation and description of the factual data if it were to be improved and modified. Such

[79]Agricola, *De natura eorum quae effluent ex terris* (1546), pp. 519–20.
[80]"All excellent things have always been worthy of being diligently contemplated. And this applies to natural objects more than all others, because with the cognition of the latter it seemed that man acquired an indefinable something beyond that which seemingly was allotted to the human species" (*De natura eorum*, p. 510).
[81]Agricola, *De metallica*, p. xxx.

a description must be systematic, analytic, and meticulous. Special illustrative techniques were required to translate the results of observation into the clearest and most comprehensible graphic images possible. It was this desire for clarity, this precise will to avoid mistakes, to place oneself deliberately at a distance from the fabulous view of things, that a work like Vesalius' *De fabrica* and Agricola's *De re metallica* had in common. In neither can we discern a full presentation of the new method which shows an awareness of the implications of its own premises and is thereby capable of contributing modifications to the theoretical systemization of the particular sciences. Their significance is to be seen elsewhere, in the capacity, by way of a "recourse to nature" and the elaboration of communicable descriptive techniques, which placed the traditional frames of a knowledge in which systematic observation was considered as a "marginal" or "secondary" activity into a crisis situation.[82] We need only consult those treatises on herbs, or the bestiaries, or those compilations of natural facts with which medieval literature abounds, or consider those listings and descriptions of animals, plants, metals, and stones which enjoyed a great popularity during these years, to get an idea of the enormous distance which separates Agricola's attitude from that found in those natural encyclopedias

[82]For a consideration of the work of Vesalius which takes these aspects into account see A. R. Hall, *The Scientific Revolution*, p. 51: "The normal development of any established department of science may be, and indeed usually is, conditioned in large part by its conceptual structure in exceptional situations, however, . . . the apprehension of the import of a whole group of facts may force a crisis. . . . Through the effort of Vesalius . . . there was introduced into biological science for the first time an acute sense of the importance of minutiae, of the mastery of special methods, and of precise and full reporting of observations." On the importance of illustrations for the formation of a habit of precise observation see G. Sarton, *The Appreciation of Ancient and Medieval Science during the Renaissance* (Philadelphia, 1955): "The Illustrations were not simply valuable in themselves; their existence close to the text must eventually lead to the correction of the latter. It became more and more objectionable to reproduce stereotyped words in the vicinity of correct images" (p. 93).

against which he had assumed a clearly polemical position. What was important in those encyclopedias was the description of "secret and rare things"; the "facts" dwelt upon were invariably exceptional, curious, and out of the ordinary. Heraldic animals were listed among real beasts; living creatures were classified on the basis of the element in which they were thought to live (air for birds, water for fish, fire for salamanders); information was taken almost exclusively from classical sources; and finally, legends were introduced and fantastic etymologies created.

The *Minera del mondo* (Venice, 1589), by Giovanni Maria Bonardo, can be taken as a typical example of this kind of literature.[83] The preference for "rare and secret" things was made known by the title. Mountains, baths, lakes, metals, gems, trees, plants, worms, "minute tiny creatures," serpents, fishes, and birds were presented in alphabetical order. But the absolute lack of a system, the inability to make the observations revolve around an organized body of knowledge, and the indiscriminate acceptance of a certain literary tradition endow such books with the characteristic tone of fable: "Atop Palombra mountain there is a marvelous fountain. Whoever drinks of it never suffers any illness and always seems young for as long as he lives."[84] Even where a descriptive intent predominated, it always appeared intertwined with the recounting of "marvelous" facts. From this point of view Bonardo's description of amber is typical:

Amber if first rubbed by a cloth attracts to itself leaves, straws, fibers, and the hems of clothing. But if the straw and fiber are first rubbed with garlic, the amber cannot attract them. It reveals poisons in two ways, having this property from nature, by exhibiting a clash of colors and by emitting certain signs

[83]*La Minera del mondo dell'il Signore Gio. Maria Bonardo nella quale si tratta delle cose piu' segrete e piu' rare de' corpi semplici nel mondo elementare e de' corpi composti inanimati et animati* (Venice, 1589).
[84]*Ibid.*, p. 10.

after the manner of a rainbow. If you wish to know whether your wife is faithful, keep it in water for three days and then give her this water to drink. . . .[85]

It was not a question of "popular" superstitions but rather a resumption of themes which had found an expression in the traditional literature of those who wrote treatises on stones and gems.

Another more famous and more widely circulated book published in England in 1756 presents attitudes very similar to those of Bonardo. This work, *A Greene Forest* by John Maplet, carried the formidable subtitle description "wherein may be seene the soveraigne virtues of all kinds of stones and metals, next of plants as of herbes, trees and shrubs; lastly of brute beasts, fowls, creeping wormes and serpents and that alphabetically."[86] Here the term *naturall history* was used in English for the first time, but it was an encyclopedia of genuine medieval flavor, compiled largely on the basis of *De proprietatibus rerum* by Bartolomeus the Englishman, and in which the fantastic etymologies of Isidor of Seville were reproduced: "The cat in Latin is called catus, as you would say *cautus*, warie or wise."

The attitude toward natural reality assumed by Agricola is antithetical to that outlined here, but in order to grasp this we would have to examine his precise and lucid classifications, which are more than his programmatic declarations, and which are also very explicit in tone: "I have omitted all those things which I had not myself seen, or have not read or heard from persons upon whom I can rely."[87] The criticisms that Agricola levels at the procedures

[85]*Ibid.*, p. 19.

[86]J. Maplet, *A Greene Forest, Wherein May Be Seene the Soveraigne Virtues of All Kinds of Stones and Metals, Next of Plants as of Herbes, Trees, and Shrubs; Lastly of Brute Beasts, Fowls, Creeping Wormes and Serpents, and that Alphabetically* (London, 1576). The citation is taken from C. T. Onions, *Natural History in Shakespeare's England* (Oxford, 1950), vol. I, p. 477.

[87]Agricola, *De re metallica*, pp. xxx–xxxi.

of alchemy are particularly interesting from this point of view and much more decisive than those of Biringuccio.[88] According to Agricola, up to then the art of metals had been the object of very few studies. He cites Biringuccio among the handful of authors who had seriously dealt with the characteristics of various metals, the structure of metalliferous sites, and the procedures required for extracting metals from the subsoil. The very scarcity of these investigations made it appear to him "all the more wonderful that so many alchemists have arisen who would compound metals artificially, and who would change one into another." Agricola does not dare explicitly to deny the possibility of a transmutation of metals, but nevertheless he assumes an outright ironic stance toward the claims of the alchemists:

These masters teach their disciples that the base metals, when smelted, are broken up; also they teach the methods by which they reduce them to the primary parts and remove whatever is superfluous in them, and by supplying what is wanted make out of them the precious metals—that is, gold and silver. . . . Seeing that so many writers assure us with all earnestness that they have reached the goal for which they aimed, it would seem that faith might be placed in them; yet also seeing that we do not read of any of them ever having become rich by this act, nor do we now see them growing rich, although so many nations everywhere have produced, and are producing, alchemists, and all of them are straining every nerve night and day to the end that they may heap a great quantity of gold and silver, I should say the matter is dubious. . . . They would have by today filled whole towns with gold and silver.

But the deepest meaning of his criticism is not in pointing out this irony in an activity in which men who were culturally much more significant than Agricola were to con-

[88]On Biringuccio's uncertainties with respect to alchemy we have a precise attestation (which, I believe, has never been noted) from the historian Benedetto Varchi: "I spoke about alchemy with M. Vannuccio Biringuccio of Siena, with whom I was already very friendly in Florence while he was working on that big artillery piece which later in the vernacular was called the arquebus of Signor Malatesta. . . . In sum he talked about alchemy in a very confused and irresolute way, as he still does, as can be seen in his writings." B. Varchi, *Questione sull'alchimia* (Florence, 1827), pp. 63–64.

tinue to show an interest. He is much more profound when
he dwells on the deliberate obscurity of language and the
arbitrary character of the alchemist terminology. Agricola
protests against this arbitrary character in the name of a
knowledge that is communicable and whose language has
the characteristics of precision and intersubjectivity: "There
are many other books on this subject, but all are difficult
to follow, because the writers on these things use strange
names, which do not properly belong to the metals, and
because some of them enjoy now one name and now
another, invented by themselves, though the thing itself
changes not." What he energetically rejects, above all, is
the transformation of the investigation of nature into an
attempt to arouse stupor and wonder, and to bend scientific
research toward ends of personal glory. "Even their books
proclaim their vanity, for they inscribe in them the names
of Plato and Aristotle and other philosophers, in order that
such high-sounding inscriptions may impose on simple
people and pass for learning.[89]

At this point the break with several characteristic attitudes of alchemy is total, indeed definitive. Several characteristics of scientific research emerge negatively from
Agricola's insistence on those aspects of precision and communicability that are indispensable to technical knowledge.
All, or almost all, alchemists' texts emphasize the theme
that the language of alchemy was "occult," "secret," and
"miraculously communicable." Only by considering the per-
sistency of this stress is it possible for us to understand
more precisely the meaning of the criticisms leveled at the
alchemists by Agricola: "All these alchemists employ obscure language, and Johannes Aurelius Augurelli of Rimini,
alone has used the language of poetry." In this way he
dealt with one of the most widely propagated texts of
medieval alchemy;[90] and the "extraneousness" of the lan-

[89]For the citations in this paragraph see the Preface to Africola,
De re metallica.

[90]M. Petri Boni Lombardi Ferrariensis, *Introductio in artem Chemiae in tegra, ab ipso authore inscripta Margarita Preciosa Novella,
composita ante annos plus minus ducentos septuaginta*, Montisbeli-

guage here theorized was in no way viewed as deriving from its technical character but from its inability to communicate truths except by a transference of notions from soul to soul, which was to be effected through miraculous and extraordinary ways: "This therefore is the discourse of alchemist philosophers. Since it is written in obscure and enigmatic terms and in unusual and impossible illustrations, what should we say of the research of the finality of the investigation and of the attainment of the same finality on the basis of this same kind of communication? This attainment seems almost impossible to me except by way of word of mouth and divine inspiration."[91]

Indeed, there was to be an insistence on these themes at the peak of the Renaissance on the part of Cornelius Agrippa, who was not alien to technical problems and to the "invention of machines."[92] To understand magical discourse it is necessary to have recourse to a trusted teacher who will use sacred words: "The meaning is other than that transmitted by letters: veiled by many mysteries and not yet openly explained by some of the teachers. And I do not know whether someone, without a trusted and ex-

---

gardi apud Jacobum Foillet (1602), p. 132. On this work, composed in Pola in 1330, and on its circulation, see L. Thorndike, *A History of Magic*, vol. III, pp. 147–62.

[91]M. Petri Boni, *Introductio in artem Chemiae*, p. 123. A passage on p. 157 is very significant: "Nunc dicimus et vere firmamus quod nullus antiquorum, a primo homine usque ad ultimum, potuisset secretum istius artis divinum adinvenire suo ingenio naturali secundum rationem naturalem solam nec secondum experientiam, cum ipsum supra rationem et experientiam consistat ut quid divinum occultum."

[92]Cf. in H. C. Agrippa, *Opera* (Lugduni, 1600), vol. II, p. 863, letter of Sept. 1526 (Ep. IV, 44): "Vero scribo nunc pyromachiam et non tam scribo, quam ipsa experimenta ostendo; jamque habeo apud me non modicis sumptibus paratos architecturae et bellicarum machinarum meae inventionis. Modulos admodum utiles simul et perniciosos et quales hactenus (quod sciam) nostra vidit aetas." But also cf. vol. II, p. 910 (Ep. V, 20) of Dec. 1527: "Mittimus tibi cum residuis machinis pontem nostrum, opus quidem rude et abortivum ac proportione carens, ingenio tamem et industria facilitateque haud contemmendum."

pert teacher, can understand such a meaning only by way of reading books, unless he be illuminated by the divine name, something which is granted few. These things in fact are not confided to letters, nor written with the pen, but they are infused by the spirit through sacred words."[93]

When we bear in mind the weight of formulations of this type in the culture of the Renaissance, the attitude assumed by Agricola toward the alchemist tradition appears historically more significant than might be considered at first. Recall that among the "philosophers" who were contemporaries of Agrippa there were figures such as Patrizzi, Paracelsus, Cardano, and della Porta, that the alchemist tradition appears largely dominant in all the treatise literature dealing with "metals," and that in the face of these problems the very cultivators of strictly technical problems had assumed positions less advanced than those of Agricola.

There is finally a third theme which Agricola, in *De re metallica*, confronts with great clarity and precision and which is of notable cultural import, namely the defense of mining against the charge of being "unworthy and base" in comparison with the liberal arts. The two charges against which Agricola intended to defend himself were: (1) that which contended that metal industries were "fortuitous" and, (2) that which claimed it was a servile, "sordid toil, unworthy of a free man or an honest and honorable gentleman." The first charge tended to reduce the activity of the technician to the level of a manual activity "requiring not so much skill as labor" and which consequently had to forgo any claim to being scientific. The second charge, reflecting an opinion going back to Aristotle, arrived at the same result by setting technics, understood as manual labor, in opposition to science conceived as a disinterested contemplation of conceptual truths.

Agricola countered this twofold charge by showing that the activity of the "technician" entailed a whole series of

[93]H. C. Agrippa, *Opera*, vol. II, p. 904.

relations with various sciences, and that it could not be separated from an actual mastery of the several fields of knowledge. The "mineralogist" had to be expert in identifying terrain, and distinguishing the veins, the various species of stones, gems, and metals; as well as know about "the various systems of assaying substances and of preparing them for smelting . . . and here again there are many altogether different methods." But the miner must likewise be knowledgeable about philosophy so that "he may discern the origin, cause and nature of subterranean things;" about medicine, so that "he may be able to look after his diggers and other workmen, that they do not meet with the disease to which they are more liable than workmen in other occupations"; about surveying, arithmetical science, and architecture, so that "he himself may construct the various machines and timber work required underground, or that he may be able to explain the method of construction to others"; the art of drawing; and finally, he must also have a knowledge of law.[94] Hence the work of the technician can in no way be separated from that of the scientist. In reply to those who based themselves on the Aristotelian distinction between free men and slaves in order to array scientific research against the work of the technician, Agricola militantly asserted:

Certainly if mining is a shameful and discreditable employment for a gentleman because slaves once worked mines, then agriculture also will not be a very creditable employment, because slaves once cultivated the fields; nor will architecture be considered honest because some slaves have always been found skillful in their profession; nor medicine, because not a few doctors have been slaves. Nor will any other worthy craft, because men captured by force of arms have practiced it.[95]

We find an equally passionate defense of the dignity of the mechanical arts, based on reasons similar to those

[94]Agricola, *De re metallica*, pp. 2ff.
[95]*Ibid.*, p. 23.

advanced by Agricola, in the *Mechanicorum libri* by Guidobaldo del Monte (1545–1607):

But inasmuch as this word "mechanics" is perhaps not understood by everyone in its true meaning, indeed we can find some
who deem it to be a term of insult (it being customary in many
parts of Italy to call someone a mechanic in scorn or abuse
just as there are some who wax indignant if they are called
engineers), it would be amiss to recall that "mechanic" is a
most honorable word . . . fitting to a man of lofty enterprise
who with his hands and judgment knows how to bring to completion marvelous works that are of singular usefulness and
delight to human existence.[96]

Although it indiscriminately recalled the pseudo-Aristotelian
Mechanical Problems and Archimedes, Guidobaldo's con-
cern was to defend the wholly mechanical character of
Archimedes' work against a famous passage in Plutarch:

Although Plutarch . . . asserts that Archimedes despised mechanical arts as sordid and ignoble, that he never deigned to
write commentaries on them, and that he worked in mechanics
not as a matter of importance but as mere amusement, . . .
nevertheless, we read in other authors that he had dictated a
book on the measure and proportion of every manner of vessel,
devising the form of the great ship built by Hiero. Pappus of
Alexandria included Archimedes' work on the equilibrium of
planes, which is the most mechanical of all, in Book VIII of his
Mathematical Collections, and the same author places an instrument for moving weights showing it to be the fortieth invented
by Archimedes. . . . His book on the equilibrium of planes is
entirely mechanical. In addition to this a part of the work on
the quadrature of the parabola and the second part of the work
on floating bodies are mechanical. In these places, therefore, we

[96]Guidobaldo del Monte, *Mechanicorum libri VI* (Pesaro, 1577).
The citations in the text are from an Italian translation: *Le Mecaniche dell'illustrissimo Sig. Guido Ubaldo de' Marchesi del Monte, tra-
dotte in volgare dal Sig. Filippo Pigafetta, nelle quali si contiene la
vera dottrina di tutti gli istrumenti principali da mover pesi gran-
dissimi com picciola forza*, printed (Venice, 1581) by Francesco di
Franceschi of Siena. See in connection with this and the two citations immediately following the unnumbered pages of the dedication: *Guidobaldo a' lettori*.

see it expressed that Archimedes not only fashioned mechanical devices, but also wrote many treatises on them.

Indeed, Plutarch himself had to admit that Archimedes' fame was linked to his mechanical undertakings which had obtained for him "the renown of more than human sagacity." Plutarch's error, once more, derived from a prejudice against the arts of mechanics.

To destroy such a prejudice, Guidobaldo pointed out how utlity and nobility work jointly to adorn the mechanical disciplines, and how the latter originate from the harmonious conjunction and the congruous communion of geometry and physics. In mechanics, geometry achieves its complete fulfillment, and through mechanics, man achieves mastery over physical and natural things. Whatever is helpful to artisans, artists, peasants, and mariners is encompassed in the realm of mechanics. From its development and by its progress in time, man has derived the plow and the means of transporting goods, oars, and the rudder, the means of raising water for irrigation, oil and wine presses, the felling of trees and marble-cutting, and the techniques of fortifications and of military siege.

Following the pseudo-Aristotelian *Quaestiones*, Guidobaldo viewed nature as a reality that could be mastered, even cheated through the astuteness of intelligence and labor, up to the realization of those "miracles" wrought by art which are not included in the immediately "natural" order of things. "Hence being a mechanic and engineer is an office of a worthy and lordly person, and 'mechanics' is a Greek word signifying something done with artifice so as to move very great weights with little force, as if by miracle and beyond human potency. In general it includes every building, tool, instrument, winch, device, or contrivance masterfully wrought and worked on for such effects and infinite other things similar to them in which it is desired to combine science, art, and practice."[97] This same

[97]Guidobaldo del Monte, *Le Mecaniche*, and *Guidobaldi a' lettori*.

conception of the relationship between art and nature, against which Galileo was to polemicize, appeared also in the preface written by Filippo Pigafetta in the vernacular edition of Guidobaldo's work published in Venice in 1581. Mechanics not only had the task of forcing bodies "to move from their proper sites by way of machines" and to transport them "upwards and every which way in movements contrary to their nature," but it had also to concern itself "with the elements in the universal sense and with bodies in a state of rest of motion." Thus a synthesis "of very lofty speculation and subtle manufacture" is realized through mechanics. By "speculation" the mechanic utilizes "arithmetic, geometry, astrology, and natural philosophy"; by "manufacture" he requires the "exercise and work of his hands"; and he will use "architecture, painting, drawing, and the crafts of the blacksmith, carpenter, mason, and other trades." In such a way natural philosophy, mathematics, and the manual arts were seen to cooperate in the work of the mechanic toward a single goal. Archimedes transformed mechanics from a "sordid and base art" into a noble and esteemed art, and all those from Leon Battista Alberti to Agricola and Guidobaldo, who had contributed "to revive mechanics from the dark shadows in which it lay into the clear light,"[98] lean on Archimedes.

Le diverse et artificiose machine, by Agostino Ramelli, engineer of Poland and to the king of France, was published in Paris in 1588 in a splendidly illustrated bilingual edition (Italian and French).[99] Ramelli attached only very scant importance to whether his complicated projects could actually be carried out, but he insisted on the necessity of

[98]Guidobaldo del Monte, *Le Mecaniche*, Dedication by Pigafetta (unnumbered pages).

[99]*Le diverse et artificiose Machine del capitano Agostino Ramelli del Ponte della Tresia ingegniero del Christianissimo Re di Francia et di Polonia, nelle quali si contengono varii et industriosi movimenti degni de grandissima speculazione per cavarne beneficio infinito in ogni sorte d'operatione. Composte in lingue italiana et francese* (Paris, 1588). All citations in the text are from the unnumbered pages of the Prefatione.

a "conjunction" between mathematics and mechanics. In
the preface to the work, which is dedicated to the "excellence of mathematics," Ramelli contrasted the certainty
and infallibility of mathematical reasoning to the variety
of opinions of the philosophers, i.e., "the great dispute
among the philosophers concerning the principles of natural
things." On the principles of nature "hardly three or four
philosophers would be in accord on such a subject, but if
anything is confirmed on the basis of reason by mathematicians in geometry or arithmetic, we consider it as infal-
lible and as certain as if it were pronounced by the oracle of
Apollo."

Ramelli saw in mechanical art the fount and origin of
human progress and the sign of the passage from a primitive to a civil state: "It was so necessary to men in the
very beginnings of the world, that had it been removed it
would seem as though the light of the sun had been extinguished." But this appeal "to mathematical reason" in the
writings of Guidobaldo del Monte and Ramelli did not
everywhere have the same meaning. In his commentary on
Vitruvius (1556), Daniele Barbaro appealed to mathematics in order to establish the greater or lesser "scientific
authority" of a particular branch of knowledge. In contrast
to his other writings, in this work he ended up reintro-
ducing the distinction between technics and science, and
separating once more "discourse" and "reasoning" from
"practice" and "manual" dexterity.

The arts that serve, with dignity and greatness, the convenience and use of mortals—such as the art to travel by sea
called navigation, the military art, the art of building, medicine,
agriculture, hunting, painting, sculpture, and similar activities—can be considered in two ways. First, by how they are
discussed and how, by way of reasonings, they find the causes
and the rules of operation; second, by way of working hard
on some external matter with manual dexterity. This is why
some arts have more science and others less. But the following
criterion enables us to know the more worthy arts: all those
which require the arts of numbering, geometry, and mathe-

matics—all such arts have a quality of greatness about them. The rest, without the aforementioned arts (as Plato says), is sordid and baser than something born of mere imagination, a fallacious conjunction and experience forsaken by the truth.[100]

The reference to Plato is not casual. Barbaro was to sing a hymn of praise to the "force of proportion," to the "divine force of numbers," and to the "consonance of the weight of number and of measure" which preside over the "structure of this university that we call the world" and regulate "time, space, movements, virtues, speech, artifice, nature, and knowledge."[101] But in his Platonism, the image of mechanics as a synthesis of the "loftiest speculation" and of "subtle manfacture" ended up by being destroyed. For Barbaro the defense of the mechanical arts turned out to be an attempt to show that in reality they were "liberal," being linked more to the arguments of mathematics than to the work of the hands.

The actual union between "discourse" and "practice," "speculation" and "manufacture," in reality presented serious problems. For example, an engineer like Bonaiuto Lorini, who served as a military technician with Cosimo de'Medici and for the Republic of Venice, was perfectly aware of their importance and their methodological significance. In his treatise *Delle fortificazioni* (Venice, 1597), he grappled with the problem of the relation between the work of the purely speculative mathematician" and that of the "practical mechanic." The demonstrations and proportions found by the mathematician "between surface lines and imaginary bodies and separated from matter do not respond so perfectly when applied to material things," because the concepts with which the mathematician works "are not subject to those impediments which by nature are

[100]*I dieci libri dell'Architettura di Vitruvio, tradotti e commentati da Monsignore Barbaro* (Venice, 1556), p. 7.

[101]*Ibid.*, p. 57. The best bibliography of writings by and on Barbaro is in the Russian edition: *Desiat knig ob arkhitekture Vitrouvia s Kommentariami Daniele Barbaro,* ed. V. P. Zoubov in collaboration with other scholars (1938).

always conjoined to the matter that is worked on by the mechanic." The mechanic's judgment and ability consists in knowing how to foresee the difficulties deriving from the diversity of the materials with which he must work, and this is all the more difficult in that no such rules can be offered for "such accidental impediments":

Indeed, the material itself could present a very great impediment, as would be the case when material wheels have to be moved around their axes, which can be impeded by their own unequal weight, even more so when the wheels are sustained over such axes or poles that are not properly centered, all of which can tend to make motion difficult. The pure mathematician, however, imagines them as weightless and tied around invisible lines and points.[102]

Galileo Galilei's *Discourses on Two New Sciences* was to revolve around this problem of the relations between the "imperfections of matter" and the "purest mathematical demonstrations."

[102]Bonaiuto Lorini, *Delle fortificazioni*, V.

Chapter Two

The Idea of Scientific Progress

A definite way of viewing science was gradually being formed and strenghtened during the great scientific and philosophical revolution of the seventeenth century. Although it has been under attack from many quarters and for many reasons, manifestly this view of science is still present and operative in the culture of the contemporary world. This view that science is an edifice, constructed laboriously in slow stages, which is never really finished and to which each one can make his contribution to the limits of his powers and capacities. Collaboration and cooperation are thought to be essential for the progress of science and require the creation of appropriate social and linguistic "institutes." The aim of scientific inquiry is not to secure the advantage of an individual person, race, or group but that of the whole human race, and in every case the development of the growth of research itself is more important than the individual persons who actualize it. All these propositions, which in the course of time *became* axiomatically accepted truths, at first were but elements among others that formed part of an approach to science; the historical origins of which can be precisely determined. For example, this approach is totally absent from the great conceptions of the Orient, classical antiquity, and medieval scholasticism. It came to light in Europe as a natural prod-

uct of modern western civilization between the mid-sixteenth and mid-seventeenth centuries.[1]

The appeal to "nature" and "experience" so widespread
in the culture of the Renaissance (what type of knowledge
and what culture, after all, do not appeal to a certain
"nature" and to a certain "experience"), the rejection of
authority (Aristotle, Galen, Ptolemy), the "disputation" with
the "ancients," and insistence upon the necessity of observation as such do not of themselves imply acceptance of this
ideal view of science. This ideal has a public, democratic,
and collaborative character, composed of individual contributions organized in the form of a scientific discourse
and offered with the view of achieving a general success
which becomes the patrimony of mankind.

This conception of science, which found its first expression on a "philosophical" plane in the work of Francis
Bacon, played a crucial role in the formation of the idea
of progress, for it implied several things. The first of these
is that scientific knowledge increases and grows, being
actuated through a process to which generations of scholars
successively contributed. Second is that this process, or any
of its movements or stages, is never complete, being ever
needful of successive additions, revisions, or integration.[2]
Third is that in some way there is a single scientific tradition, for science does not present itself as an assemblage
of theories and "isms" set in opposition to each other, but
as a process in which even the most revolutionary upheavals
"salvage" the kernel of truth acquired by previous generations and present themselves as theories of a more general
character in which the earlier theories are subsumed as
particular stages or cases of scientific progress.[3]

The idea of progress, and the view of scientific knowl-

---

[1]E. Zilsel, "The Genesis of the Concept of Scientific Progress," in
Roots of Scientific Thought, ed. P. Wiener and A. Noland (New
York, 1957), p. 251.

[2]*Ibid.*, p. 252.

[3]For a discussion of this last point, see L. Geymonat, *Filosofin e
filosofia della scienza* (Milan, 1960), pp. 111ff.

edge on which this idea depends, originated in Europe at
a time when a grandiose series of discoveries was greatly
modifying man's mode of living and thinking. These discoveries gave rise to the impression of a new forward thrust
by man which seemingly coincided with the acceleration
of history itself. Campanella expressed this most vividly:
"Oh, if you knew what our astrologers say of the coming
age, and of our age, that it has in it more history within
a hundred years than all the world had in four thousand
years before, of the wonderful invention of printing and
guns and the use of the magnet. . . ."[4]

It was the moment when the discovery of new lands and
the widening of the frontiers of the world provided a mode
of "testing" the doctrine of the ancients and of putting a
finger, as it were, on its limitations. Furthermore, there
was a growing clarification of the concept, on which
humanist philosophy had already insisted for so long, that
antique philosophy and science were not necessarily collections of eternal verities. Rather, they were historical products linked to a particular time and place, being valid,
satisfactory, and fully legitimate for men *at that time*. But
they were no longer declared to be valid, satisfying, or
legitimate in a new and different historical situation in
which, in the face of novelties and novel problems, different questions were being posed requiring new and more
articulate answers.[5] Belleforest wrote in the *Histoire des
neuf rois Charles:*

The voyages of modern times have shown that the ancient
astronomers and geographers had a scant knowledge and even
less experience, inasmuch as they had the brazenness to con-

---

[4]T. Campanella, *City of the Sun.* The translations in the text are
taken from C. M. Andrews, ed., *Famous Utopias* (New York, 1901).

[5]Agricola, *De inventione dialectica,* I, 3: "Aristolelem . . . sum-
mum quidem hominem, sed hominem tamen fuisse puto." On this
and similar passages and on the significance of the work of the
humanists see the numerous studies on the subject by E. Garin, esp.
Medioevo e Rinascimento (Bari, 1954), pp. 207–10.

tend that the world beyond the equator was uninhabited, but-tressing their contention with cold and frivolous reasons. Happy is our century to have men like our voyagers, and still happier these mariners for having been born in a time when the activity of such excellent men is esteemed by kings and honored by those of mediocre fortune.[6]

The ancients, wrote Le Roy in 1575, believed "that it was impossible to pass easily from one temperate zone to the other because of the torrid zone; instead, as a result of voyages and navigations there has come the realization that the whole earth is inhabited."[7] Jacques Cartier made an even more pointed observation: "The common naviga-tors of our day, making real experiments, have learned the opposite of the opinions of the philosophers." The theme of the limited character of the cultural horizon of the ancients was combined with another, upon which we have dwelt at length, namely, that of the superiority of experi-mental over bookish knowledge.

I have seen one of our pilots, Jean de Meun, a native of Harfleur, albeit an illiterate, make such progress in the art of navigation through maps and astrolabes that, invariably, he reduced to silence an educated man who had embarked with us and who discoursed about theory with a haughty air. But it is not for this reason that I condemn or censure the knowledge acquired in the schools through books. . . . Still, regardless of anybody's opinion, I would like to ask that nobody try to con-vince me of something that is contrary to experience.[8]

A new empiricism came into being as a result of contact with a new world, an empiricism based on the observation of the life of plants, animals, men formerly unknown, and a non-Christian society, of the viability of coexistence with

[6]Fr. de Belleforest, *L'histoire des neuf Rois Charles de France* (Paris, 1568), p. 417.
[7]L. Le Roy, *De la vicissitude ou varieté des choses en l'univers* (Paris, 1575).
[8]J. Cartier, *Bref récit et succincte narration* (Paris, 1545), p. 2; *Histoire d'un voyage en Brésil* (La Rochelle, 1578), pp. 38–39.

atheists and primitive ignorance innocent of sin. It was linked to the concept of a "nature" that was no longer homogeneous and uniform but different from one region of the earth to another and one that could not be fitted into the framework of traditional knowledge.[9] Yet, from an historical and ethicopolitical point of view, this awareness of the unity of the world and of the human race, finally achieved, was in keeping with a conception of nature that no longer exhibited the feature of uniformity. After the widening of the frontiers of the world, asserted Le Roy in his *Considérations sur l'histoire universelle* (1567), the events of human history can only be encompassed within a unitary frame. In his glorification of the new age, Le Roy drew a significant comparison between the great inventions of technology and the great geographical discoveries. According to him the clarification of minds that revealed the limitation and the insufficiency of the wisdom of the ancients derived from this twofold resolution:

[After the voyages and the discoveries] . . . [T]he affairs of the world, linked in reciprocal correspondence, cannot be understood or explained in a perfect history, the one without the other. It seems to many that such a link and such a general correspondence between Europe, Asia, Africa, and the New World is tending toward some extraordinary effect. . . . We observe that there has never been, in the past, a century in which culture and the liberal arts have arrived at a perfection

[9]Cf. I. B. Cohen, "La découverte du nouveau monde et la transformation de l'idée de la nature," in *L'expérience scientifique au XVIe siècle* (Paris, 1960), pp. 189–210. On these themes, see: G. Chinard, *L'Amérique et le rêve exotique dans la littérature francaise au XVIIe et au XVIIIe siècle* (Paris, 1913); *L'exotisme américain dans la littérature française au XVIe siècle* (Paris, 1911); G. Atkinson, *The Extraordinary Voyage in French Literature before 1700* (New York, 1920); *The Extraordinary Voyage in French Literature from 1700 to 1720* (Paris, 1922); V. Pinot, *La Chine et la formation de l'esprit philosophique en France, 1640–1740* (Paris, 1932); G. Atkinson, *Les nouveaux horizons de la Renaissance française* (Paris, 1935); R. Roneo, *Le scoperte americane nella coscienza italiano del Cinquecento* (Milan-Naples, 1954); W. Kaegi, *Meditazioni storiche* (Bari, 1960), pp. 216–37.

greater than that of today. Not at the time of Cyrus I, in which
lived Pythagoras and Thales; not at the time of Alexander the
Great, when Greece produced all that which was loftiest in
letters, in arms, and in all the arts; not in the time of Augustus,
. . . not in the time of Saracens when Averroes, Avicenna, and
Abenzoar lived. In the last hundred years not only have things
come into view which were first covered by the shades of
ignorance, but many other things have been known which the
ancients had completely ignored: new seas, new lands, new
types of men, habits, laws, customs, new herbs, trees, minerals,
new inventions such as those of the printing press, artillery, the
compass, and ancient languages have been rediscovered.[10]

The new astronomy made a major contribution to this
sense of the limited character of the "truths" discovered by
the ancients. By widening the frontiers of the universe
beyond measure, in some cases going even so far as to
assert an infinite universe, it produced the precise sensation that accompanied the awareness of the end of all
traditional views and considerations of the cosmos.[11] As
John Donne wrote in 1611:

> And new Philosophy calls all in doubt,
> The Element of fire is quite put out;
> The Sun is lost, and th'earth, and no man's wit
> Can well direct him where to looke for it.
> And freely men confesse that this world's spent,
> When in the Planets, and the Firmament
> They seeke so many new; then see that this
> Is crumbled out againe to his Atomies.
> 'Tis all in peeces, all cohaerance gone;
> All just supply, and all Relation.[12]

[10]L. Le Roy, *Considérations sur l'histoire universelle* (Paris, 1567),
pp. 8–9.

[11]On this crisis see E. M. W. Tillyard, *The Elizabethan World
Picture* (London, 1943); V. Harris, *All Coherence Gone* (Chicago,
1949); M. H. Nicolson, *The Breaking of the Circle* (Evanston, 1950);
A. Koyré, *From the Closed World to the Infinite Universe* (Baltimore,
1957), pp. 28ff.

[12]J. Donne, "Anatomy of the World" in *First Anniversary* (1611),
(New York, Nonesuch ed.), p. 202.

Pierre Borel asserted in 1657, in a volume treating the new astronomical discoveries,

We perceive that we know nothing that is not or cannot be debated, even theology is not exempt from it, and insofar as the other sciences and arts, the books that we have bear witness. This has induced the Pyrrhonists or Sceptics to doubt everything and has given birth to diverse books on the vanity of the sciences. Astronomy, medicine, jurisprudence, and physics vacillate every day and see their very foundations crumble. Petrus Ramus has destroyed Aristotle's philosophy, Copernicus Ptolemy's astronomy, Paracelsus' Galenic medicine. So that, each one having his followers and all seeming plausible . . . we are compelled to admit that that what we know is much less than what we do not know.[13]

Not a few poets, writers, and philosophers of the first part of the seventeenth century had the precise sensation of an exhaustion of the world, of the superannuation of the universe, of the end of a culture, of the deep crisis into which had been plunged a whole way of understanding man and nature and the place of man in nature. "Our century," wrote Mersenne to Peiresc on March 12, 1644, "is the progenitor of a universal upheaval. What do you think of these upheavals, are they not perhaps a prefiguration of the end of the world?"[14]

The existence of a grandiose turning point in knowledge capable of arousing men to states of exaltation and enthusiasm or, as more often happened, of stupor and bewilderment, was thus confirmed. Also confirmed was the necessity, perceived in many quarters, of a new knowledge, corresponding to the new dimensions of the geographical

[13]P. Borel, *Discours nouveau prouvant la pluralité des mondes* (Geneva, 1657), pp. 3–4.
[14]Many testimonies on the "decreptitude of the world" are collected in H. Haydn, *The Counter-Renaissance* (New York, 1960), pp. 525–44. Mersenne's letter to Rivet is published in part in R. Lenoble, *Mersenne et la naissance du mécanisme* (Paris, 1943), p. 342.

world and of the astronomical universe. The term *novus* recurs in the titles of literally hundreds of scientific books published in the course of the seventeenth century.[15] It was not only a question of a literary form. Rather, it was the vehicle for the significant expression of the exigencies, disquietudes, and discontents of an age that had perceived the inadequacy of the traditional modes for the formation of man.

> Oui, mais on parle en l'air, et n'est rien la science
> Au jour d'huy que des mots, sans que l'expérience
> Qui la doit esclairer de pres comme son jour
> Ait l'honneur seulment de la suivre à son tour:
> De Grec et de Latin, mais point de connaissance
> On nous munit la teste en notre adolescence[16]

2.

We can discern the first, albeit rudimentary, formulations of the new concept of science and scientific progress in many texts written by the "master craftsmen" and the engineers of the sixteenth century. As justifications for their work, the technicians advanced the glory of God and public utility. And this work was viewed as something which would be added to an already existing fund of knowledge destined to be prolonged, perfected, and integrated in time through the cooperation of others. Edgar Zilsel, in a felicitous image, has contrasted the workshop, arsenal, and *bottega*, which were places where men worked together, to a monk's cell and a humanist's study. Zilsel draws conclusions from this contrast that are not wholly acceptable. But we can agree with him when he points out that the

[15] A very broad list of the term in this connection is found in L. Thorndike, "Newness and Novelty in Seventeenth-Century Science," in Wiener and Noland, eds., *Roots of Scientific Thought*, pp. 443–52.

[16] Perrot de la Salle, *Le mystère des asnes* (Lyon, 1599), pp. 3–4. See also A. M. Schmidt, *La poésie scientifique au seizième siècle* (Paris, 1938).

birth of capitalism and the economic competition led those men to theorize goals in connection with their work which were very different and certainly more impersonal than those of individual santification or literary immortality.[17]

The awareness of the further perfectibility of one's work, of the necessity of intellectual cooperation and of the progressive character of knowledge in time is clearly evident in passages in many "technical" books written in the sixteenth century. In the dedication to Pirckheimer, serving as a preface to his *Vier Bücher von menschlicher Proportion* (1528), a treatise on the proportions of the human body, Dürer clarifies the reasons why a nonscholar such as himself dared consider so lofty a theme. He decided to publish the book "risking slander for the public benefit of all artists and in order to induce other experts to do likewise so that our successors may have something to perfect and lead to further progress, and so that the art of painting can achieve its perfection in the course of time."[18] Without the new inventions, asserts the German geographer Apianus in *Quadrans astronomicus* (1532), "life would return to the state of the ancient man who lived without laws or civilization, similar to beasts." Consequently, "those who reject better things for the simple reason that they are new" are greatly in error.[19] Accused of having betrayed guild secrets, the Paris surgeon Ambroise Paré (1510–1590), an autodidact who had no Latin and who, furthermore, was hated by the faculty, bravely replied that he did not belong to the category of those who "make a cabala of art." The texts of the ancients, he asserted, should serve us only to see further. We must not rest on the labors of the ancients [since] there are more things to be discovered than have

[17]E. Zilsel, "The Genesis of the Concept of Scientific Progress," p. 237.

[18]A. Dürer, *Vier Bücher von menschlicher Proportion* (Nuremberg, 1528), Dedication.

[19]P. Apianus, *Quadrans astronomicus* (Ingolstadt, 1532), Dedication.

been discovered up to now . . . and the arts are not so perfect that additions cannot be made to them; they become perfect and better in the course of time."[20]

Simon Stevin (1558–1620), a military engineer and technical adviser to Maurice of Navarre, published his *Mémoirs mathématiques* so that "his errors might be corrected and other inventions added, inasmuch as the joint effort and the work of many scholars is required in this field."

We find similar theses expressed in a passage of Daniel Barbaro's commentary on Vitruvius' treatise on architecture (1556):

With the name of God glorious, I, Daniel Barbaro, a noble Venetian, have taken upon myself the task of expounding and interpreting the ten books on architecture by Vitruvius. My intention has been to be of utility to students of technical inventions and to give an opportunity to others to write more clearly on those matters which for some reason may have escaped from my hands. . . . The birth of Art is weak at the beginning, but with time it acquires strength and vigor. The first inventors have little light concerning things and cannot gather many universal propositions through which Art might grow, since they have no time to test them because of life's brevity; but by leaving to posterity the things discovered by them, they reduce the work of the latter and in addition give them the opportunity to increase their Arts.[21]

The military engineer Agostino Ramelli expressed himself with even greater clarity on this problem. The mechanical arts, he wrote in the preface to *Le diverse et artificiose machine* (1588), were born of the labor and the needs of the first men who built the first "mean hovels to protect themselves against the inclemency of the sky, from the ravages of the seasons and from the many harms of the earth," and they covered their bodies "to expel from

[20]A. Paré, *Oeuvres* (Paris, 1840), vol. I, pp. 12, 14.
[21]*I dieci libri dell'Architettura de' Vitruvio tradotti e commentati da Monsignor Barbaro* (Venice, 1556), pp. 5–6.

themselves the moist rains, the impetuousness of the winds, the fervent heat of the sun, the bitterness of the cold." According to Ramelli, the successive development is not akin to the motion of the winds which are born in vehemence and which thereupon progressively diminish in intensity until they vanish. Rather, it is similar to the course of rivers whose beginnings are small and weak but which arrive at the sea fully grown and powerful after being enriched by the water of the tributaries.[22]

3.

In many cases these assertions regarding the perfectibility of art were only the echo of ancient doctrines already present in the texts of Aristotle, Hippocrates, Seneca, and Averroes. But the idea in those texts was not that of a knowledge that is indefinitely, progressively enriched. Rather, they propounded the quite different idea that no science arrives at its perfection through the work of a single individual. Science could continue to present itself as a self-enclosed and perfect reality which is not all perfectible to infinity. The limitedness of the process ended up by rendering the notion of the progressive character of science futile and illusory.[23]

It would be difficult to say at what point the assertions contained in the technical treatises of the sixteenth century were free of the burden of these attitudes. What is beyond

[22]A. Ramelli, *Le diverse e artificiose machine* (Paris, 1588), Preface.

[23]On this problem see Garin, *Medioevo e Rinascimento*, p. 196. The picture drawn by Zilsel in "The Genesis of the Concept of Scientific Progress" is partial and insufficient because this theme is not discussed. Important limitations of his thesis are found in A. C. Keller, "Zilsel, the Artisans and the Idea of Progress in the Renaissance," in Wiener and Noland, eds., *Roots of Scientific Thought*, pp. 276–80. Among Zilsel's other writings connected with these problems see "The Sociological Roots of Science," *American Journal of Sociology* (1942), pp. 544–62; "Problems of Empiricism: Experiment and Manual Labor," *International Encyclopedia of Unified Science* (Chicago, 1951), pp. 53–94.

doubt, however, is that the common and concordant insistence upon the progressive and collaborative character of the arts and the affirmation that knowledge grows on itself in time and is enriched in the process from the work of many, like a river by its tributaries, cannot be explained merely by recalling classical texts. Here, the recognition of the ever novel results produced by the arts led to the affirmation that the cultural horizon of the ancients was a limited one which, at the same time, stressed the provisional and historical character of their discoveries. This affirmation, which appears in about ten texts by theorists of navigation and in the journals of voyagers, was destined in turn to be subverted into the other, namely superiority of the moderns which was to achieve great renown and give rise to a dispute of a singular and passionate character.

The champions of the superiority of the moderns and those who contended that the moderns were not inferior with respect to the ancients (from Bodin to Vico) were mainly to avail themselves of two arguments in defense of their thesis: (1) the findings of technics which have deeply modified human life are the living demonstration of the progress achieved by the human race; and (2) the great geographical discoveries which have unified the world, making it like one big, single city, have thus exposed the narrow and confining character of the city in which the ancients lived and operated.

Blaise de Vigenére wrote:

Many infinitely beautiful things of which the ancients were ignorant have been discovered: the compass, for the lack of which so many ships were lost at one time, and the art of printing which is the most admirable and divine invention the human mind ever conceived. These inventions can be opposed to that which the previous centuries possessed of the rarest and most exquisite character. . . . It is reasonable to make a place for antiquity, but from this it does not at all follow that we must read or see or praise or approve only the works of the ancients.[24]

[24]Blaise de Vigenère, Preface to N. Chalcondoyle, *L'histoire de la décadence* (Paris, 1571).

This text appeared in 1571. Five years earlier in the "Methodus ad facilem historiarum cognitionem," Bodin had proclaimed that not only the virtues but the knowledge of the moderns shines as brilliantly as that of antiquity. The present epoch, he continued, has seen minds think with a fecundity such as had never been seen before:

But the ancients, it will be said, nevertheless remain the inventors of all the arts and by this qualification they well deserve their glory. We shall gladly acknowledge that they have discovered many sciences useful to the human race, beginning with the notion of celestial bodies; they have studied the regular course of the heavenly bodies, the admirable trajectories of the stars and planets; struck by the obscurity of nature, they have studied her with care and they have come up with an explanation of many problems. But they also have left behind many unsolved problems which we pass on completely solved, to our descendants. And, where we look more closely, there is no doubt that our discoveries surpass those of the ancients. What, for example, is there more marvelous than the magnet? The ancients were ignorant of it and were ignorant of its marvelous use and had to restrict themselves to the Mediterranean basin while our contemporaries every year sail around the world with their sea-crossings and have colonized, so to speak, a new world. Not only has a prosperous and profitable commerce derived therefrom . . . but men have linked themselves to one another and marvelously participate in the universal Republic as if they formed a same city. . . . The secrets of nature have been disclosed and salutary medicines discovered. I shall not speak of the method of determining longitude . . . nor of the catapults and of ancient instruments of war which, compared to ours, are children's toys. I shall set aside the innumerable industries of metal and fabrics which are so marvelously useful to human life. The art of printing alone would easily be able to match all the inventions of the ancients.[25]

The rejection of the myth of a golden age of the human race and of an ancient, unreachable, arcane wisdom was born of this recognition of the revolutionary significance of

[25]J. Bodin, "Methodus ad facilem historiarum cognitionem," in *Oeuvres Philosophiques de J. Bodin*, ed. P. Mesnard (Paris, 1951), pp. 227–28.

the great inventions of the moderns. An image of the primitive was emerging which later was to be adopted by Hobbes and Vico. That rejection and this image by itself underlined the reality of progress: "Let us take a look, therefore, at these ages of gold and silver. Men at that time lived scattered in fields and forests like wild beasts and possessed only that which they could hold through force and crime. It required much time to lead them, little by little, away from this barbaric and savage life toward civil customs and a well-regulated society and to the present humaneness of customs."[26]

A few years later, in *De la vicissitude ou varieté des choses en l'univers* (1577), Louis Le Roy again dwelt on the importance of inventions and on the unity finally achieved by the whole human race: "The whole world is now known and all the races of man. Men can now reciprocally exchange their inventions and reciprocally help each other in their needs like the inhabitants of a same city."[27] But even nine years earlier, in *Les politiques d'Aristote* (1568), which was contemporaneous with the *Considérations sur l'histoire universelle*, Le Roy had dwelt on the thesis of the progressive growth of knowledge. "The arts and sciences receive their perfection not by leaning on the sayings and opinions of men of earlier ages, no matter how great their authority may be, but by correcting them and modifying them every time they do not appear good. . . . Great things come to light slowly; they are not manifested all at once and contemporaneously but are perfected with the passage of time."[28] In the text published in 1577, the doctrine of progress is expressed with greater clarity:

Things did not come to a stop with what the first men had done, said, or written, but the generations have also made their contribution and things have been discovered and illuminated with the passage of time. . . . If the ancients had not written

[26]*Ibid.*, p. 226.
[27]L. Le Roy, *De la vicissitude*, p. 7.
[28]L. Le Roy, *Les politiques d'Aristote* (Paris, 1568), Preface.

or said anything that already had not been said or written before them, no art would have ever been invented and all would have remained in their first phases without ever growing. . . . Nothing forbids this age to produce men like Plato and Aristotle in philosophy, or like Hippocrates or Galen in medicine, or like Euclid, Archimedes, and Ptolemy in mathematics, . . . and if we view things properly, there is no century more felicitously disposed to the progress of culture than ours.[29]

In a famous passage of *La cena delle ceneri* (*Ash-Wednesday Supper*), 1584, Bruno theorized on the superiority of the Copernican view of the cosmos as compared to that of the ancient astronomers. To the pedant Prudentio, who repeats the ancient adage, "The sage says wisdom is in antiquity," Bruno (who speaks through Teofilo) replies:

And he [the sage] added: Prudence is in many years. If you really understood what you just said, you would draw the very opposite conclusion from this principle. I am of the opinion that we moderns are older and therefore have at our disposal riper experiences than the ancients, our predecessors, for the judgment of such questions as we have before us. It would have been impossible for the judgment of Eudoxus, who still lived in the infancy of astronomy, to be as ripe as that of Calippus, who lived thirty years after the death of Alexander the Great; for the same reason a Hipparchus could know more than Calippus, since he had an overview of the whole development which had taken place in the 196 years since the death of Alexander. The Roman mathematician Menelaos, who surveyed the difference of the motions in the 462 years since Alexander's death, could judge things better than Hipparchus. The astronomer Mohamed Aracenslis was bound to know more 1202 years later. But in our day Copernicus has a span of 1849 years at his disposal since that time.[30]

On the basis of this passage, the Italian philosopher Giovanni Gentile hailed Bruno as an isolated champion of the historicity of the mind. But the fragility of such a con-

[29]L. Le Roy, *De la vicissitude,* last ch.
[30]G. Bruno, *Dialoghi italiani,* edition prepared by Gentile and Aquilecchia (Florence, 1958), pp. 39–40.

clusion has been amply demonstrated by now. Moreover, this Gentilian distortion has been counteracted by the opportune stress that has been laid on the theologico-naturalistic themes present in Bruno's thought. Scholars have also rightly dwelt on Bruno's integral reduction of the course of history to an eternal, cyclical event, to "a revolution that is vicissitudinal and yet eternal" which strips the temporal and historical process of meaning. In the attempt to make of Bruno a precursor of idealism not a few historians have preferred to eliminate a theme that was central to his thought: "In nature there is a revolution and a circle . . . all that rises must likewise fall . . . a lofty and magnificent vicissitude, which raises the interior to the superior waters, changes night into day and day into night, so that divinity may be in all." When Bruno quoted from *Ecclesiastes*— "*Quid est quod est? Ipsum quod fuit. Quid est quod fuit? Ipsum quod est. Nihil sub sole novi.*"—before the tribunal of the Inquisition, he was affirming that all things "cannot be other than what they have been, nor will they be other than what they are . . . and only separation, or conjunction, or composition, or division, or translation occurs."[31]

But in those pages on astronomy, with which Bacon perhaps was familiar, we find the ancient thesis according to which no science arrives at perfection. In that chronology of astronomers, excerpted from Copernicus' *De revolutionibus*, Bruno laid stress on the progressive accumulation of "observations" added to "observations" in the forward march of science. The final exactness of his language—"for the judgment of such questions as we have before us"— is not without significance. Here Bruno is making a reference to scientific knowledge, and in particular to astronomy.[32] In

[31]Cf. G. Gentile, *G. Bruno e il pensiero del Rinascimento* (Florence, 1920), pp. 87–110; reprinted in *Il pensiero italiano del Rinascimento* (Florence, 1940), pp. 331–55; A. Corsano, *Il pensiero di G. Bruno nel suo sviluppo storico* (Florence, 1940), pp. 56–61; E. Garin, *Medioevo e Rinascimento* (Bari, 1954), pp. 195–201; G. Aquilecchia, Preface to *La cena delle ceneri* (Turin, 1955), pp. 56–59.

[32]This aspect has been stressed in Aquilecchia, *La cena*, pp. 34, 57.

an earlier passage of the *Ash-Wednesday Supper*, he had referred to the work of "industrious mathematicians who in the course of time, adding light to light,"[33] have furnished sufficient proof for the acceptance of the Copernican system. These are themes which, although they do not allow us to draw the untenable and paradoxical conclusion that Bruno was a champion of the idea of progress (perhaps, indeed, the only champion), nevertheless, they warrant comparison with those passages in *The Expulsion of the Triumphant Beast* which have rightly been viewed as a glorification of labor as the means by which man emerged from his primitive bestial condition and as a vindication of "the full dignity of man's technico-economic activities, and of his effort at the transformation and production of things in the face of a harsh, unpropitious nature."[34] The dignity of man is not entrusted (as with Ficino and Pico) only to the ascending power of his intellect, but also to "action by means of his hands." Further,

The gods had given intellect and hands to man and had made him similar to them, giving him power over other animals. This consists in his being able not only to operate according to his nature and to what is usual, but also to operate outside the laws of that nature, in order that by forming or being able to form other natures, other paths, and other categories with his intelligence—by means of that liberty . . . he would succeed in preserving himself as god of the earth. . . . And for that reason Providence has determined that he be occupied in action by means of his hands and in contemplation by means of his intellect, so that he will not contemplate without action and will not act without contemplation.

In the so-called golden age men once lived in a bestial state, being neither more virtuous nor intelligent than animals are today. But "now that difficulties have been born and needs have arisen among them, because of their emulation of divine acts and their adaption to inspired affects,

[33]Bruno, *Dialoghi italiani*, p. 27.
[34]Corsano, *Il pensiero di G. Bruno*, pp. 197–98; cf. F. Battaglia, *Filosofia del lavoro* (Bologna, 1951), pp. 86–93.

their minds have become sharpened, industries have been invented, skills have been discovered, and always through necessity from day to day new and marvelous inventions are summoned forth. . . ."[35]

The work of the hands—the "solicitous and urgent occupations," industries and the arts—viewed as an emergence from bestial being, tends toward an approximation of the divine condition. It is truly difficult to recast the unity of Bruno's thought, and there is no point in looking *a posteriori* for the linear coherence and placid continuity in what appears now as its haunting manifestation of conflicting themes which, not by chance, took the form of the dialogue.[36] The celebration of the slow accumulation of science through the work of generations did not exclude a cyclical view of this historical event; the recognition of the dignity of *making*, of operations that subdue nature, did not prevent Bruno from returning, in the *Heroic Frenzies*, to the ancient thesis that men were divided into two groups, where the existence of men who work with their hands and of "mechanics" serves to justify the existence of contemplative minds and of philosophers: "It is necessary that there be artisans, mechanics, farmers, servants, pedestrians, the ignoble, the base, the poor, the pedants, and others of the sort; for otherwise there could not be philosophers, saints, educators, lords, captains, noblemen, illustrious men, wealthy men, wise men, and others who are as heroic as the gods."[37]

Virtually the whole work of Francis Bacon addressed itself to the task of replacing a culture of a rhetoric-literary type by a culture of a technico-scientific type. Bacon was perfectly aware that the realization of this program of reform in-

[35]G. Bruno (*Spaccio della bestia trionfante*), *The Expulsion of the Triumphant Beast*, tr. Arthur D. Imerti (New Brunswick, N. J., 1964), p. 205.

[36]Garin, *Medioevo e Rinascimento*, p. 197.

[37]G. Bruno, *The Heroic Frenzies* (*Degli eroici furori*), tr. Paul Eugene Nemmo (Chapel Hill, N. C., 1964), p. 21.

volved a break with tradition, and he was firmly convinced of two things: that in order to effect this break it was necessary to make a historical examination of the past; and that such a break involved not only man's mode of thinking but his way of living and his attitude toward the natural world and cultural tradition. According to Bacon, the type of philosophical discourse elaborated in the classical world posited the superiority of a life of contemplation over a life of work, of resignation to nature rather than the conquest of nature, and of introspective reflection over direct investigation of facts and things. For him the issue was to produce a crisis in that type of culture where philosophical discourses of the classical type were considered legitimate and possible and on this foundation to arrive at a definition of the tasks, methods, and ends of a philosophy different from that which for centuries had presented itself as consubstantial with philosophical inquiry.

All of Bacon's work (and even the less perceptive among his interpreters have noticed this) calls for a total reform and is based on the conviction of a radical change immanent in human history. This change is in no way identical to a transformation of philosophy, for it does not concern speculation alone: the "advancement of learning" does not derive from the intense toil of philosophical schools or sects; it is closely connected with the whole situation of civilization. When Bacon spoke of his work as a "birth of Time rather than birth of Wit," he was not simply using a rhetorical device but was expressing a deep personal conviction. The historical change that interested him, and to which he considered he could make pertinent his work as philosopher and organizer of culture, depended on a series of material factors which, in his opinion, have incalculable weight in the world of culture. Inventions, the reflowering of the mechanical arts, geographic discoveries, voyages of exploration, and new political conditions of Europe had changed the conditions of life on earth. Bacon understood that this would involve a change in the mode of thinking in philosophy: "It would be disgraceful if while the regions of the material globe—that is, of the earth, of the sea, and of the stars—have been in our time laid widely open and revealed, the intellectual globe should remain shut up within the narrow limits of old discoveries."[38]

Three great inventions—the compass, the printing press, and gunpowder, seemingly had so radically changed the course of history that in Bacon's view "no empire, no star seems to have exerted greater power and influence in human affairs than these mechanical discoveries." Indeed his protest against the "barrenness" of the traditional culture was focused on the opposition it set up between the mechanical arts and philosophy, between progressiveness— the hallmark of technico-scientific knowledge—and the ignobility that typified the dialectical exercises of the Schools and the rhetorical exercises of Humanism:

For twice a thousand years the sciences stood where they did and now remain almost in the same condition, receiving no noticeable increase, but on the contrary, thriving most under their first founder, and then declining. Whereas in the mechanical arts, which are founded on nature and the light of experience, we see the contrary happening, for these (as long as they are popular) are continually thriving and growing, as if the breath of life inspired them—at first rude, then convenient, afterwards adorned, but at all times advancing.[39]

Within the framework of the traditional philosophies, Bacon argued, every assertion has remained an assertion, every question has remained such, and "instead of being resolved by discussion is only fixed and fed." Although the philosophical and intellectual sciences are "worshipped and celebrated" as if they were idols, their progress has been abso-

[38]*Novum organum*, I, 84. All references to Bacon's writings, except for the *Novum organum*, indicated by the book and paragraph, refer to *The Works of Francis Bacon*, in seven volumes, ed. R. L. Ellis, J. Spedding, D. D. Heath (London, 1857–1874).

[39]*Novum organum*, I, 74; cf. *Works*, III, pp. 289–90 (*Advancement of Learning*); *Works*, I, pp. 457–58 (*De augmentis*).

lutely nil, whereas the progress of the mechanical arts has been so swift "that men would sooner leave the study in pursuit of them to turn to something else, before they arrive at the ultimate perfection."[40] According to Bacon, this progressiveness which is the hallmark of the mechanical arts depends upon a very special situation, namely the fact that in them the "wits" of many collaborate toward a single end: ". . . in mechanical arts the first deviser comes shortest, and time addeth and perfecteth." There is no room for the dictatorial powers of the individual in the mechanical arts, but only for the power of a "senate" which does not demand that associates give up their freedom by turning themselves into prostrate and perpetual slaves of a single person. In the mechanical arts "many wits and industries have contributed into one; yet in the latter [the liberal arts and sciences] many wits and industries have been spent in the cause of the wit of some individual, whom many times they would have rather depraved than illustrated." Thus time works in favor of the arts whereas, on the contrary, it contributes to the destruction of the initially perfect edifices constructed by the philosophers. With the passing of the centuries the philosophies and sciences of Aristotle, Plato, Democritus, Hippocrates, Euclid, and Archimedes have become "degenerate and impassed."[41]

In the mechanical arts knowledge is progressive; it grows on itself. Collaboration among its investigators constitutes its predominant characteristic. These fields of knowledge must be characterized by progressiveness and collaboration, and only in such a way will man possess a criterion capable of clearly differentiating science and technics from every knowledge of a "magical" type. Bacon repeatedly asserts that his projected method of science does not reserve a great role for the genius of the individual and, as it were, equalizes minds: "But the course I propose for the discovery of

[40]*Works*, I, p. 126 (Preface to *Instauratio magna*).
[41]*Works*, I, pp. 457–58 (*De augmentis*), and cf. *Works*, III, pp. 289–90 (*Advancement of Learning*).

sciences is such as leaves but little to the acuteness and strength of wits, but places all wits and understandings nearly on a level. For as in the drawing of a straight line or a perfect circle, much depends on the steadiness and practice of the hand, if it be done by aim of hand only, but if with the aid of rule or compass, little or nothing; so is it exactly with my plan."[42] Some interpreters have understood this assertion as the expression of optimistic faith in the mechanical character of a method which, once set in motion, would have functioned by itself. There has been no lack of passionate protests against this demand "to compel the infinite richness of thought to run along a one-gauge track."[43] But, as often happens, indignant protests were the product of scanty and superficial historical knowledge. If we bear in mind the cultural background which spawned this assertion, we realize that it is an expression of hostility toward the characteristics of uniqueness associated with the methods employed in magico-alchemist investigations. In the latter, as Agricola had already pointed out and as Bacon reiterated, the result seemed to depend exclusively on the application of a secret procedure which, in turn, was due to the extraordinary abilities of an individual.

This is why Bacon set the figure of the teacher in opposition to that of the inventor, and the figure of the illumined sage to the man who advances learning by the addition of his personal contribution to the work of those preceding him. In contrast to that which occurs in the mechanical arts, the tradition of the various disciplines "is still a succession of masters and scholars, not of inventors and those who bring to further perfection the things invented."[44]

From this point of view the contrast that Bacon established between the moderns and the ancients, as well as his polemic against the "fascination with antiquity" which like

[42]*Novum organum*, I, 61; cf. *Works*, III, 250 (*Valerius terminus*); also III, 638 (*Filum labirinthi*); III, 572 (*Redargutio philosophiarum*).
[43]G. de Ruggiero, *Storia della filosofia: l'età cartesiana* (Bari, 1939), p. 41.
[44]*Works*, I, 126 (Preface to *Instauratio magna*).

a spell prevents men "from entering into contact with real things," acquires a more exact meaning. To accept tradition and succumb to this fascination has consequences of an incalculable significance in Bacon's view. For that path leads to an acceptance of the characteristic position of the past: the transformation into ontology of one's own technical inadequacy. The Aristotelians had placed "whatever is beyond their own or their master's knowledge or reach . . . as beyond the bounds of possibility." By so doing they "most presumptuously and individually" turn "the weakness of their own discoveries into a calumny on nature herself, and the despair of the rest of the world."[45]

The ancient philosophers, in particular the Aristotelians, have constructed a philosophy of nature in terms of the deficiency of their instruments of control and mastery over nature. Writes Bacon: "Not for nothing we have opposed our modern 'There is more beyond' to the 'Thus far and no further of antiquity.' The thunderbolt is inimitable, said the ancients. In defiance of them we have proclaimed it imitable, and that not wildly but like sober men, on the evidence of our new engines."[46]

On these bases, antiquity can truly appear as the youth of the world and the present era as old age which has a greater knowledge of human affairs and a greater maturity of judgment since "it is enriched by infinite experiments and observations." In a paragraph of the *Novum organum*,[47] which is often quoted in isolation from a more general context, Bacon seems to appropriate the thesis of the aging and the decrepitude of the world—a thesis very widespread in Shakespeare's time. In the general context of his discourse, progress appears as the hope of a march never before made by the human race. "Indeed, I exert myself in behalf of those things to the hazard of others. . . . I ask men to come forward themselves and take part in that which remains to be done." And in the *Redargutio philosophiarum* Bacon wrote:

[45]*Novum organum*, I, 75, 84.
[46]*Works*, III, 579 (*Redargutio philosophiarum*).
[47]*Novum organum*, I, 84.

I foresee for myself a destiny like that of Alexander. . . . While his memory was fresh his exploits were regarded as portents. . . . But when the admiration had cooled and men looked more closely into the matter, note the sober judgment passed upon him by the Roman historian. "All Alexander did was dare to despise shams." Something like this later generations will say of me. Emancipated, masters of themselves, having learned by experience their own powers, they will forge far ahead of my first steps.[48]

Several typical categories of technical knowledge—collaboration, progressiveness, perfectibility, and invention—became categories to which Bacon attributed a universal value. They must serve to define the whole field of human knowledge. By taking the mechanical arts as a model for culture, by basing ourselves on the characteristics of progressiveness and intersubjectivity that marked part of the work of technicians, it is possible, according to Bacon, to give rise to a type of culture which, in contrast to ancient culture, is susceptible to progress. In it, the work of mechanics and empiricists will be conjoined with that of the philosophers, and in this way surpass that "Mechanic, often merely empirical and operative, which does not depend on Physics" and which is entrusted only to "patience and the subtle and ruled motions of the hand and instruments."[49]

On this point Bacon is very clear: "The empirical school of philosophy gives birth to dogmas more deformed and monstrous than the sophistical or rational school." True philosophy is born of the conjunction of the work of the "empiricists" and that of the "rationalists." In the celebrated parable of the ants, spiders, and bees in which Bacon speaks of the "pure empiricists" who do not go beyond the collection of data, he was referring specifically to the mechanical arts: "The genuine philosopher should not extract his material from natural history and mechanical experience, and not take it unaltered into the memory, but

[48]*Works,* III, 584 (*Redargutio philosophiarum*).
[49]*Novum organum,* I, 85; *Works,* I, 572 (*De augmentis*).

digest and assimilate it for storing in the understanding."[50]

"The alchemists," writes Bacon in *Cogitata et visa*, "grow old and die embracing their illusions; the achievements of the magicians are unsure and fruitless; the mechanical arts draw little light from philosophy, though they do gradually enlarge the humble web woven by experience. Chance without doubt is a useful originator of things, but scatters her blessings on mankind only after tedious and tortuous wanderings." Collaboration between science and technics is to replace chance and "gross observations." The transformation of reality, the installation of the *regnum hominis* cannot be entrusted only to fire but must be entrusted to reason which works with the aid of instruments. As Bacon asserts in heavy imagery: "Man must forsake Vulcan[51] in order to entrust himself to Minerva."

4.

The same year in which the *Novum organum* was published, there was also published *Dieci libri di pensieri diversi* by Alessandro Tassoni (1620). Tassoni's work supported

[50]*Novum organum*, I, 64; *Works*, III, 582 (*Redargutio philosophiarum*).

[51]*Works*, III, 591 (*Redargutio philosophiarum*); *Novum organum*, II, 7. For information on the principal works dealing with Bacon's philosophy, see Appendix Two. See also P. Rossi, *Francis Bacon: from Magic to Science* (London, 1968); "Per una biblografia degli scritti su F. Bacone, 1800–1956," *Rivista critica di storia della filosofia* (1957), pp. 75–89.

The following studies were published after 1957: P. H. Kocher, "Bacon on the Science of Jurisprudence," *Journal of the History of Ideas* (1957), pp. 3–26; R. McRae, "Unity of the Sciences: Bacon, Descartes, Leibniz," *Journal of the History of Ideas* (1957), pp. 27–48; L. Aneschi, "Bacone tra Rinascimento e Barroco," *Rivista di Estetica* (1957), pp. 322–45; J. G. Crowter, *Francis Bacon, the First Statesman of Science* (London, 1960). The work by E. de Mas, "F. Bacone e il De Sapientia," *Rivista Internaz. di filos. del diritto* (1957), pp. 393–412, takes no account of the only serious work on the subject—that of Charles Lemmi—and is perfectly useless. Of greater interest is a recent article "Bacone e Vico," *Filosofia* (1959), pp. 505–59. See also the two articles by V. De Magalhaes-Vilhena on "Bacon et l'antiquité," *Revue philosophique* (1960, 1961).

the thesis of the superiority of the moderns—in addition to citing the inferiority of the pagan religion with respect to the Christian religion—with the argument of the perfecti-bility of the arts and sciences. The assertion, traceable to Seneca, of the original imperfection of the arts which are gradually refined and perfected through intelligence and industry, did not impress Tassoni as a sufficient argument to "terminate this quarrel in favor of modernity." Arts and doctrines do not progress always in conjunction "with a consistent development of minds." Rather, at times they fall into the hands "of people of slow and weak intellect which set them back, at other times they are extinguished and are absolutely lacking." This is what happened in Italy, according to Tassoni, when the country fell into the hands of the barbarians for many centuries. Pestilences, wars, and droughts destroy men and extinguish the arts. The latter have a "birth and youth and perfection" as well as "an old age and death; and just as at times they grow and spread in leaps and bounds, so can it come to pass that at times they can vanish in an instant."[52]

Thus Tassoni recognized the possibility of awesome throwbacks in human progress. He dwelt at length on the desultory character of the march of human affairs and on the threat of decrepitude and death to which the arts were constantly exposed. His interpretation of the Middle Ages as the age of barbarism and obscurantism made him skep-tical of every form of illuminist faith in the advancement of learning. For him, classical culture constituted the para-digm and model of every culture. Nevertheless, the new light that in his time shone so resplendently over Italy, and the general renewal of minds, enabled him to strike a com-parison between the new and the ancient culture to the advantage of the moderns. The thesis of the superiority of

[52]A. Tassoni, *Paragone degli ingegni antichite moderne* (1918–1919), pp. 101–02; on Tassoni and the criteria he employs to sus-tain the thesis of the superiority of the moderns, see H. Naef, *Due contributi all storia dei Pensieri di A. Tassoni* (Trieste, 1911).

the moderns drew aid and comfort from the observation of those marvelous inventions in technics which were unknown to the antique world:

What did the Greeks and Romans ever invent that can be compared to the printing press? . . . This noble invention which has introduced a procedure thanks to which the souls of glorious men may never die on earth? Let us pass on to the compass and to the nautical chart . . . if the Romans gloried in the transport of their armies to the island of England by way of the ocean. . . . What glory is owed to him who taught the Portuguese to navigate to an unknown pole, from one horizon to another? . . . Now I come to military machines. What invention so tremendous was ever imagined that could match that of our artilleries? . . . What would the Greeks and Latins have said of the most brilliant invention of wheel clocks that strike and show the hours in a perpetual round, as well as the motions of the planets? The telescope alone, recently invented in Flanders and perfected in Italy, with which you can see things fifteen or twenty miles away as though they were in front of you and which discovers invisible stars in the sky, surpasses by far any Latin and Greek inventions that were discovered in the whole of the so-much celebrated course of years.[53]

Many writers laid stress on the "miraculous" character of inventions. We would certainly have remained incredulous, wrote Pierre Borel in 1655, if we had been assured through the printing press it would have become possible "to write an infinity of books—in a brief span of time and with a velocity a thousand times greater than that with which we speak and transmit our conceptions to posterity thereby acquiring a sort of immortality." Borel, a collector of alchemist and chemical texts, and a supporter of the theory of the plurality of worlds, had a greater awareness than did Tassoni of the decisive importance of the technical revolution. With the telescope he saw the symbol of the victory of human ingenuity over nature, and the sign of the superiority of the moderns. "Let, therefore, ancient Athens keep silent with her famous lyceum, let the fables go untold

[53]Tassoni, *Paragone degli ingegni*, pp. 144–45.

according to which men exist whose eyes penetrate the bowels of the earth and perceive treasures and waters. Today the most notable and truest lynx eyes have appeared from whose sight nothing can escape."[54]

Charles Perrault, ushering in the great *Querelle des anciens et des modernes* (1688-1697), asserted that progress depends on the slow accumulation of knowledge in the course of time. Beyond partial defeats and provisional lapses, the march of the human race is a perpetual and indefinite growth.

Read the journals of France and England, the publications of the Academies, and you will realize that more discoveries in the science of nature have been made in the last twenty or thirty years than in all the period of antiquity. . . . Those who have come last have, as it were, gathered the legacy of their predecessors and have added to it a great number of new acquisitions due to their labor and their toil.[55]

In France, however, the Quarrel of the Ancients and the Moderns revolved more around the literary merits of the writers and poets of the classic age and of those of the century of Louis XV than it did around the progress of natural philosophy and of the mechanical arts:

> La docte Antiquité, dans toute sa durée
> A l'égal de nos jours me fut point eclairée
> Et l'on peut comparer, sans crainte d'être injuste
> Le siècle de Louis au beau siècle d'Auguste.

This polemic, which had been sparked on linguistic and literary terrain, was derived by setting the centuries in opposition to each other, which ended by directly affronting

[54]Borel, *Discours nouveau prouvant la pluralité des mondes*, p. 5.
[55]On the *Querelle*: Frailh, *Histoire des querelles littéraires* (Paris, 1771); H. Rigault, *Histoire de la querelle des anciens et des modernes* (Paris, 1856); H. Gillot, *La querelle des anciens et des modernes en France* (Paris, 1914); G. Margiotta, *Le origini italiane della querelle des anciens et des modernes* (Rome, 1953); E. Garin, *L'educazione in Europa* (Bari), pp. 273-97.

the great themes of modernity and progress. But it touched only marginally on the problems connected with the progress of science and technics. Boileau, in a polemical exchange with Perrault, was very explicit on this point: "Your intent was to show that because of its knowledge, above all because of the fine arts, our century or, better said, the century of Louis the Great was not only comparable but also superior to the most famous centuries of antiquity and indeed to the century of Augustus." It was not by accident that the dispute centered around the worth of certain Greek and Latin classics. In the *Réflexions critiques sur Longin* (1694), Boileau stubbornly defended Pindar and Homer, and in a ferocious epigram accused the disparagers of Homer, Plato, Cicero, and Virgil of impiety:

> Pour quelque vain discours sottement avancé
> Contre Homère, Platon, Ciceron ou Virgile,
> Caligula par tout fut traité d'insensé,
> Neron de furieux, Hadrien d'imbécile.
> Vous donc, qui dans la même erreur,
> Avec plus d'ignorance, et non moins de fureur
> Attaquez ces Héros de la Grece et de Rome;
> Perrault, fussiez-vous Empereur,
> Comment voulez-vous qu'on vous nomme?"[56]

Fontenelle also stressed the fact that "eloquence and poetry were the essence of the Quarrel of the Ancients and the Moderns." Still, what clearly emerged in his work was the concept of the continuity of knowledge and indefinite progress: "One cultured mind composed, so to speak, of all the minds of previous centuries: one mind alone has been

---

[56]N. Boileau, *Réflexions critiques sur quelques passages de Longin en lettre à Monsieur Perrault*, in *Oeuvres diverses du Sr. Boileau Despreaux* (Amsterdam, 1702), vol. II, pp. 109–83, 185–98. The epigram cited is in vol. I, p. 253; but on the same page:

> D'ou vient que Ciceron, Platon, Virgile, Homère
> Et tous ces grands auteurs que l'Universe révère,
> Traduits dans vos Ecrits nous paroissent si sots?
> Perrault, c'est qu'en prêtant à ces Esprits sublimes.
> Vos façons de parler, vos bassesses, vos rimes
> Vous les faits tous des Perraults.

educated during all this time. . . . Men will never degenerate, and the sound views of all the good minds that will
succeed each other will be added each to the other. We are
in a century in which the arts seek to draw profit from the
new lights of philosophy." And a real progress is registered
only in the name of scientific knowledge. The ancients may
be superior to the moderns in eloquence and poetry, which
Fontenelle concedes depends on the imagination, but in
science, profit can be derived from the errors of others and
"the last physicists and mathematicians are perforce the
most able."[57]

Several English authors of the latter half of the seventeenth century arrived at similar conclusions independently
of Fontenelle. In contrast to what happened in France, in
England the Quarrel of the Moderns and the Ancients,
which served as a background to Jonathan Swift's celebrated satire, revolved around the current themes of natural
philosophy, the sciences, and the mechanical arts. Born
independently of the *Querelle*, it drew sustenance from the
forceful Baconian polemic against the method and culture
of the ancients.[58] For example, an entire section of the
Apologie by George Hakewill (1627) was dedicated to the
inventions of the moderns, and to the techniques used in
agriculture, printing, and navigation.[59] Rejecting the thesis

[57]B. de Fontenelle, *Digression sur les anciens et les modernes,* in
Oeuvres (Paris, 1767), vol. IV, pp. 179, 190; *Sur la force nécessaire
pour remonter les bateaux,* in *Histoire de l'Académie Royale des
Sciences, année 1702* (Amsterdam, 1735), pp. 167–68. On Fontenelle: J. R. Carré, *La philosophie de Fontenelle ou le sourire de
la raison* (Paris, 1932); F. Grégoire, *Fontenelle, une philosophie
désabusée* (Nancy, 1947); A. Robinet, "Considérations sur un cen-
tenaire: notes soumises aux historiens de Fontenelle," *Revue de
métaphysique et de morale* (1958); L. M. Marsak, "B. de Fontenelle:
The Idea of Science in the French Enlightenment," *Transactions of
the American Philosophical Society,* XLIX (1959).

[58]On the polemic between the ancients and the moderns in England, see R. F. Jones, *Ancients and Moderns: a Study of the Background of the "Battle of the Books"* (St. Louis, 1936).

[59]G. Hakewill, *An Apologie or Declaration of the Power and Providence of God on the Government of the World, consisting in an
Examination and Censure of the common Errour touching Nature's
perpetual and universal Decay* (London, 1627).

of the decrepitude and decay of the world, Hakewill theorized on the circularity exhibited in the progress of the arts. Joseph Glanvill, while defending the aims and functions of the Royal Society, contrasted the results of the old philosophy with that of the new experimental philosophy which opens up to man the possibility of an unbounded progress. The title of Glanvill's book is significant: *Plus ultra, or the Progress and Advancement of Knowledge since the Days of Aristotle* (1668). In this work the defense of the Royal Society was transformed into a defense of the moderns: geography, mathematics, chemistry, natural history, and inventions were so many signs of the latter's superiority. "For my part I think there is more acknowledgment due to the name of this obscure Fellow [the inventor of the compass] than to a thousand Alexanders and Caesars, or to ten times the number of Aristotles. And he really did more for the increase of knowledge, and advantage of the world by this one experiment, than the numerous subtle disputers that have lived ever since the erection of the School of Talking." On the other hand, the new islands and the new continent beyond the Atlantic have offered man "a larger field of nature."

Glanvill's argument was well defined. In a little book entitled *Plus ultra Reduced to Non Plus*, Henry Stubbe violently attacked Glanvill's work, accusing the Royal Society of wanting to replace humanistic education with a "materialistic and mechanical education" and expressing amazement over the fact that Glanvill had not gone so far as to assert the superiority of the moderns even in the field of painting and the fine arts.[60] Glanvill's reply was precise: "The controversy does not concern only the Royal Society, but must be extended to all the supporters of the moderns; a new scientific education must replace the traditional peda-

---

[60]On works by Henry Stubbe, in addition to the pamphlet cited, see preface to *Legends without Histories* (London, 1670), and *Campanella Revived* (London, 1670), in which he criticizes the idea that the study of science and mathematics distracts subjects from discussions of a political-religious character.

gogic formation." Glanvill denied that he necessarily considered the moderns superior to the ancients in the fine arts. In fact, he agreed that the opposite was true; nevertheless, he insisted that the discussion concerning progress had to be conducted on a different terrain if it were to prove meaningful.

William Wotton was even more explicit on this point. He joined the polemic waged by William Temple against Fontenelle with the publication of *Reflections upon Ancient and Modern Learning* (1694). Wotton leaned more on Glanvill's work than on Perrault's, and refused to assent to the French inclination for the superiority of the moderns in eloquence and poetry. He argued that oratory had been much more useful and encouraged within the frame of antique civilization than it was for the present; he concluded:

There are Things which have no dependence upon the opinion of men for their truth; they will admit only to fixed and undisputed works of comparison and judgment. So that though it shall always be debated, who have been the greatest orators, or who the best poets; yet it cannot always be a matter of controversie, who have been the greatest *geometers, arithmeticians, astronomers, musicians, chymists, botanists,* or the like, because a fair comparison between the inventions, observations, experiments, and collections of the contending parties must certainly put an end to the dispute.[61]

The Baconians and the defenders of the Royal Society were not the only ones in England to refer to the progress of technics and the sciences. These themes, curiously adopted to the particular exigencies of his universe of discourse, reappear in the work of the Anglican theologian John Edwards:

The diligent enquiries conducted in the homeland and the voyages to remote countries have given place to new observations and bearings as well as to extraordinary discoveries and inventions. Thereby, we surpass all the times that existed

[61]W. Wotton, *Reflections upon Ancient and Modern Learning* (London, 1694), pp. 77–78.

before us and it is highly probable that future times will surpass the present times. I confess not to understand why we
could not expect a corresponding improvement in the knowledge of God, in morality and in the Christian virtues. Can there
exist a reason why God should not allow religion to prosper
as prosper the arts?[62]

5.

The conquests of science and technology were living testimony of the superiority of the moderns; they offered the
most evident proof of the progressive character of knowledge. "Transmissible" knowledge (hence always usable and
capable of perfection) was superior to every form of solitary
spiritual wisdom. A trenchant observation has been made
that in these years a new task had arisen for the man of
culture, namely, that of intellectual collaboration.

The contacts between scholars which took place with ever
increasing frequency, the grandiose epistolaries, the great
academies, and the scientific societies of the seventeenth
century all sprang from this ideal. In 1635, writing to Peiresc, Mersenne had set forth the project of an academy that
would bring together all the learned men of Europe.[63] Ten
years before, challenging the claims of the alchemists, he
had already proposed the foundation of an academy where
"without any more mysteries or arcane procedures the
members could, in common, study the actual results of their
experiments."[64] Mersenne's faith in the progress of knowledge was closely linked to this idea of collaboration and
cooperation among the learned.

It is said that antiquity must be respected; . . . is it possible
that Aristotle, Plato, Epicurus, these great men, perhaps de-

---

[62]J. Edwards, *A Compleat History or Survey of All the Dispensa-
tions and Methods of Religion, from the Beginning of the World to
the Consummation of All the Things* (London, 1699), vol. II, p. 615.
On this defense of progress by the "religious," see R. S. Crane,
"Anglican Apologetics of the Idea of Progress," *Modern Philology*
(1934), pp. 273–306.

[63]Lenoble, *Mersenne*, p. 92.

[64]M. Mersenne, *La vérité des sciences* (Paris, 1625), p. 105.

ceived themselves? There is no consideration of the fact that Aristotle, Plato, and Epicurus were men like ourselves, of our same species, and that, moreover, the world in which we live is two thousand years older in time, that it has more experience, that it is perforce more cultured, and that, finally, it is the old age of the world and of experience that makes us discover truth.[65]

Mersenne argues further that the limit of classical philosophy—its inability to achieve real progress—was due to its character of generality, the lack of cooperation among scholars, and to the fact that each had not applied himself to a particular and limited sector of the sciences.

If our fathers and predecessors had put this precept into practice, philosophy long ago would have achieved a high degree of perfection and we would not be wasting our time today with the first difficulties which crop up now and which are as difficult as when they appeared in the first centuries, when they were disclosed for the first time. Now we would have had the experience of phenomena which could serve as the beginning of a solid reasoning, truth would not be so buried in depth. Nature would not be so hidden and we would be able to see all the marvels that she contains. . . .[66]

For the first time in history, about the middle of the seventeenth century, scholars gathered to found research organizations based on the cooperation of researchers and the publication of their findings. Such organizations were expressly constituted to make possible a systematic collaboration among scientists for the advancement and progress of the arts and sciences. This was the common aim proposed by the first modern scientific academies, namely: L'Accademia del Cimento (1657), the Royal Society (1662), and the Académie des Sciences (1666).[67]

[65]Mersenne, *Recherche de la vérité*, II, 2, 3.
[66]M. Mersenne, *Les préludes de l'harmonie universelle* (Paris, 1634), pp. 135–36.
[67]On the function and the characteristics of the academies: A. J. George, "The Genesis of the Académie des Sciences," *Annals of Science* (1938); F. A. Yates, *The French Academies of the Sixteenth*

6.

In the preface to the first edition of the *Philosophical Transactions* (1660), which brought into being one of the great collections of the scientific documents of the world, Oldenburg, a Baconian and secretary of the Royal Society, described the features and purposes of the publication:

Whereas there is nothing more necessary for promoting the improvement of philosophical matters, than the communicating to such as apply their studies and endeavors that way, such things as are discovered and put in practice by others, it is therefore thought fit to employ the press, as the most proper way to gratifie those whose enjoyment in such studies, labours and attempts of the curious and learned in things of this kind, as of their compleat discoveries and performances; to the end that such productions being clearly and truly communicated, desires after solid and useful knowledge may be further entertained, ingenious endeavors and undertakings cherished, and those addicted to or conversant in such matters may be invited and encouraged to search, try and find out new things, impart their knowledge to one another, and contribute what they can to the grand design of improving natural knowledge, and perfect in all philosophical arts and sciences. . . . All for the glory of God, for the honor and advantage of this kingdom and the universal good of mankind.

Fontenelle, who in a reference to the origins of the Académie des Sciences cited the prodigious development of the mathematical and natural sciences, also considered at length the theme of collaboration: "This widespread interest in philosophy gave rise among the learned to a desire to communicate their discoveries to each other. Indeed, more than fifty years before, those who lived in Paris used

---

Century (London, 1947); H. Brown, *Scientific Organizations in Seventeenth-Century France* (Baltimore, 1934); M. Ornstein, *The Role of Scientific Societies in the Seventeenth Century* (Chicago, 1938). On intellectual collaboration, see T. Gregory, *Scetticismo e empirismo: studio su Gassendi* (Bari, 1961), p. 176; the book is full of important observations on this order of problem.

to frequent Father Mersenne who, being the friend of the most illustrious men of Europe, was glad to act as an intermediary among them. Gassendi, Hobbes, Roberval, the two Pascals, father and son, Blondel and several others used to frequent Mersenne."[68] All that is observed, tested, studied, and learned, Fontenelle continued, must be made available to everyone, and everything must be communicated because the slow accumulation of experiment is the source and guarantee of the progress of the human race. On the basis of this new conception of science as a progressive construction based on cooperation—a never finished but always perfectible reality—a new way of viewing human history had also been in the process of formation. History could now appear as the product of a common work, the result of the effort of several generations each one of which avails itself of the labors of the preceding generations—as the slow accumulation of a series of experiments that can be successively integrated and perfected:

The first cognitions that the ancients bequeathed to us have served as steps on which to climb to our own, and it is precisely in this that we are debtors for our superiority to them; for inasmuch as we have raised ourselves up to a certain degree to which they have brought us, a slight effort suffices to climb ever higher. . . . Those whom we call ancients in truth were new to everything, and properly speaking formed the childhood of the human race. Since we have added to their knowledge the experiences of the centuries that followed them, it is in us that the antiquity which we honor in others can be found.[69]

According to Fontenelle's vision, our panorama is more extensive than that of our progenitors, since our experience takes account of their experience. It is not a question of as-

[68]B. de Fontenelle, *Histoire de l'Académie Royale des Sciences* (Paris, 1733), vol. I, p. 4.
[69]This citation, and those that follow, are taken from B. Pascal, *Préface pour le Traité du vide,* in *Oeuvres complètes,* ed. J. Chevalier (Paris, 1954), p. 534. Cf. *Opuscoli e scritti vari,* G. Preti (Bari, 1959), pp. 7–9.

serting in the abstract the superiority of the moderns; rather, we must recognize that the ancients "knew as well as we do all that which they could observe from nature," except that "they did not know as much as we, and we see more than they." It becomes possible that "without contradicting them, we can assert the contrary of what they asserted."

No doubt the spread of a thesis on which Campanella and Bacon, Le Roy and Bodin had long and unanimously insisted contributed to the assertion of these ideas: the human race had finally achieved its substantial unity in consequence of the discoveries of technics and the great voyages of exploration. "Not only does every man progress from day to day in the sciences, but all men together accomplish in them a continuous progress in the measure that the universe ages, for in the succession of generations there occurs the same thing as in the diverse ages of an individual man. Thus the whole sequence of men, in the course of so many centuries, must be considered as the same man, one who exists always and continuously learns." In this text written in 1647 and unknown to its contemporaries, Pascal gave an organic formulation to the conception of history as progress. Like Comenius and Leibniz later, Pascal had insisted on a theme of fundamental importance: the cognizing subject is not an isolated individual but "the whole of mankind which evolves progressively in time."[70]

[70]The following comprehensive works on the idea of progress were utilized for this chapter: J. Del Vaille, *Essai sur l'histoire de l'idée de progrès jusqu'à la fin du XVIIIe siècle* (Paris, 1910); J. B. Bury, *The Idea of Progress* (London, 1920); R. Hubert, "Essai sur l'histoire de l'idée de progrès," *Revue d'histoire de la philosophie et d'histoire générale de la civilisation* (1934, 1935). Among the particular studies, besides the works of Zilsel and Jones already cited: H. Weisinger, "Ideas of History during the Renaissance," *Journal of the History of Ideas* (1945), pp. 415–35; F. Diaz, "Idea di progresso e giudizio storico in Voltaire," *Belfagor* (1954); A. Cento, *Condorcet e l'idea di progresso* (Florence, 1956). The fragment from Pascal cited in the text in all probability goes back to 1647 and was published for the first time in the Bossut edition of 1779.

Chapter Three

Philosophy, Technics,
and the History of the Arts
in the Seventeenth Century

⟶⟶⟶⟶⟶

1.

Bruno had wondered why we must exert ourselves to alter and corrupt the state of nature which has "divided the world into things that are greater and things that are less, things superior and things inferior, things illuminating and things obscure, things worthy and unworthy, not only outside us but also in our very substance." The hierarchy of the faculties ended by identifying itself with the order of the universe and by codifying the necessity of an insurmountable dualism of classes and groups.[1] Yet it was precisely the will to overcome these hierarchies and these distortions that inspired Tommaso Campanella when he proposed a revolutionary program for a democratic and rational society in his *City of the Sun*. The traditional distinction between the speculative and mechanical arts is rejected for his solar city, and labor—even the most menial and humble toil—is exalted as a central and decisive element in the formation of man,

wherefore no one thinks it lowering to wait at a table or to work in the kitchen or fields. . . . Every man when told to

[1]Bruno, *The Heroic Frenzies*, p. 217; see also F. Battaglia, *La filosofia del lavoro* (Bologna, 1951), p. 92.

work who does his duty is considered very honorable. It is not our custom to keep slaves, for there are enough of us, more than sufficient for our needs. . . . And we consider him the more noble and renowned who has dedicated himself to the study of many arts and knows how to practice them wisely. Thus we are laughed at by those who consider workmen ignoble and hold those to be noble who have mastered no pursuit, but live in ease. . . .[2]

The recognition of the dignity of labor and of the mechanical arts also led Campanella to reject the class conception of society based on the opposition between "godlike" men and men who work with their hands. The excellent republic is that in which each one "is elected to perform that office into which he is born," because the communal life of men is not guided by chance but ruled by reason. All those who on the basis of their natural abilities exercise a socially productive function are, without discrimination, citizens of the republic: "We call citizens not only those who participate in the government, but all those who live together and who exercise arts useful to the republic, just as limbs of the body exercise their function. We call the rest parasites or scum (*excrementa*) of the republic, such as are many noblemen of this age."[3]

Campanella, though closely linked to magic and astrology, perceived, as did few others, the revolutionary character of the great discoveries of technics and the great voyages of exploration: "Christopher Columbus, the Genoese, saw more with his eyes and experienced more with his body than did with their minds the poets, philosophers, and theologians Augustine and Lactantius, who denied the antipodes." In the great invention of the compass, printing press, and gun powder, he saw "the signs of the union of the world," and the proof of an *acceleration* of the course of history: "Our age . . . has in it more history within a

[2]Campanella, *City of the Sun*, pp. 285, 293.
[3]T. Campanella, *Aforismi politici*, ed. L. Firpo (Turin, 1941), pp. 99, 160–61.

hundred years than all the world had in four thousand years before! And more books were produced in these hundred years than in five thousand."[4]

These inventions, which operate on and transform nature, were for Campanella the sign of the "power of man," for whom dignity and divinity do not consist only of "ascending to the sky with mathematics and of knowing the natures and measures of celestial things" but also include man's efforts "to command all terrestrial and marine things" through the art of navigation, scripture, the press, and clocks.

> E, dio secondo, miracol del primo,
> egli comanda all'imo, — e 'n ciel sormonta
> senz'ali, e conta — i suoi moti e misure
>   e le nature. . . .
> Il vento e 'l mar ha domo, — e 'l terren globbo
> con legno gobbo — accerchia, vince e vede,
>   merca e fa prede
> Merca e fa prede; a lui poca è una terra.
> Tuona, qual Giove, in guerra . . .
> . . . Egli astuto
> ha dato al cuoio muto — ed alle carte
> di parlar arte;—e che i tempi distingua
>   dá al rame lingua.
> Dá al rame lingua, perc'ha divina alma.
> La scimia e l'orso han palma, — e non si industre,
> che 'l fuoco illustre — maneggiasse; ei solo
>   si alzò a tal volo.[5]

[4]T. Campanella, *Poesie,* ed. G. Gentile (Bari, 1915), p. 86; *City of the Sun,* p. 317.
[5]Campanella, *Poesie,* pp. 170–71, vv. 17–20, 26–30, 41–48.
"A second God, miracle of the First,
He commands the depths; without wings he mounts to the heavens
And counts its motions, measures, and qualities. . . .
He masters the wind and wave; in full-sailed ship he circles the earthly globe,
He beholds and conquers all, trades and plunders,
Plunders and trades; to him the earth is little.
In war he thunders like Jove . . .
Crafty, he gives the power of speech and art to mute parchment and paper;

2.

Despite his avid curiosity with respect to the renewal of science and the new inventions of technics, Campanella, as Corsano has recently confirmed, remained essentially "alien to the great methodological and productive renovation of his age."[6] In the seventeenth century the conception of science as an intersubjective mode of learning that was communicable and was capable of progressive increment had to assert itself in a manner quite different from that of magic, and indeed in a violent polemical disputation with it. The polemic against every form of occult "knowledge," and the defense of the dignity of the mechanical arts within the world of culture, were themes that found deep response even in those quarters where the preoccupation with a theoretico-conceptual apparatus of science and the attempt to fit the natural sciences into a "scheme of rational concepts" were much more alive than they were in the times of Agricola or Bacon.

Of special interest from this point of view is the position of Descartes, who certainly did not disdain concerning himself with machines and artifices,[7] and in whose thought there appears to be no trace of the ancient condemnation of the mechanical arts. In the *Regulae*, written between 1619 and 1628, it is asserted that "there is here a resemblance between our method and the procedures of those mechanical arts which are independent of outside aid, and which themselves teach how to fabricate the tools they need."[8] The

Measuring time, he gives voice
    to brass.
He gives voice to brass, his soul is divine.
The bear and monkey have hands, but are not clever enough
To handle fire—he alone lifts himself to such heights."
[6]A. Corsano, *Tommaso Campanella* (Bari, 1961), pp. 239ff.
[7]See for example, Descartes, *Oeuvres*, ed. Adam and Tannery, vol. I, pp. 211, 435, 447; vol. IV, p. 81.
[8]*Regulae*, in *Descartes' Philosophical Writings*, tr. Norman Kent Smith (London, 1952), p. 41.

reference to the mechanical arts and to the "various crafts of the artisans" also appears in the seventh part of the *Discourse on Method,* where Descartes expressed the hope that the future may see "the invention of an infinity of arts, by which we would be enabled to enjoy without heavy labor the fruits of the earth, and all its conveniences." Here also is a forceful reiteration of the Baconian thesis of a "practical philosophy" through which men can become "the masters and possessors of nature." As a result of the general notions he had acquired respecting physics, Descartes writes, he had perceived:

that it is possible to obtain knowledge highly useful in life, and that in place of the speculative philosophy taught in the Schools, we can have a practical philosophy by means of which, knowing the force and the actions of fire, water, air, the stars, the heavens and all the other bodies that surround us as distinctly as we know the various crafts of the artisans—we may in the same fashion employ them in all the uses for which they are suited, thus rendering ourselves the masters and possessors of nature.[9]

In these passages Descartes also adopted the thesis that the publication of findings arrived at through experimentation was indispensable for the advancement of scientific knowledge: "I believed that I could not keep them [his general notions respecting physics] hidden without sinning against the law which lays us under obligation to promote, as far as it lies within us, the general good of mankind."[10] Implicit in assertions of this kind was the rejection of those "extraordinary ways" of magicians, naturalists, and alchemists who had spun theories according to which the hallmarks of knowledge were solitude and secrecy or incommunicability. In a letter written to Huygens in March, 1638, Descartes took an explicit position against every attitude of this type. And in a reference to Campanella's *De sensu*

[9]*Ibid.,* p. 151.
[10]*Ibid.*

rerum, he did not hesitate to assert that "those who go astray, affecting to follow extraordinary ways, seem less excusable to me than those who err in company and following in the tracks of many others."[11] But the company of learned men was not exactly the ideal pursued personally by Descartes.

Leibniz, in this sense truly a "Baconian," reproached Descartes for "the vanity of wishing to be a solipsist."[12] To the figure of the individual genius, capable of demolishing all and reconstructing all, he opposed the image of an integral humanity which is the true cognizing subject. Actually Leibniz's accusations were groundless, as is also the definition of the seventh part of the *Discourse on Method* as "a veritable treatise on the solitary sage" recently advanced by Lenoble.[13] A more thorough look into these pages, which seem so lucid on the surface, discloses that actually Descartes ended up by emptying of meaning his own espousal of the kind of knowledge founded on collaboration and publication of investigations with their findings. The call addressed to other minds, inviting them to contribute to the experiments that needed doing so the life and work of many might be conjoined in such a way that "we should collectively advance further than each by himself could continue to do," was essentially a call addressed by a teacher to his disciples, or by a captain of armies to his troops, obliging "all those who have the good of mankind at heart . . . to communicate to me the observations they have made, and to assist me in obtaining those that remain to be made."[14]

For Descartes, the call for collaboration was not born of the conviction of its superiority over solitary reflection but

[11]*Descartes to Huygens,* in *Oeuvres* (Paris, Gallimard ed., 1949), p. 786.

[12]A. Foucher de Careil, *Nouvelles lettres et opuscules inedits de Leibniz* (Paris, 1857), p. 13.

[13]R. Lenoble, "La révolution scientifique du XVIII° siècle," in *Histoire générale des sciences* (Paris, 1958), vol. II, p. 186.

[14]*Discourse on Method,* in *Descartes' Philosophical Writings,* p. 154.

from the awareness of the excellence of his own meditation. "But though I recognize that I am extremely liable to
error . . . no experience of the kind of objections likely to
be made to my views prevents me from looking for any
profit from them. . . . Yet rarely has it happened that anything has been objected to me which I myself had not foreseen."[15] The insufficiency of the lone individual before the
task of discovering truth stems exclusively from *de facto*
difficulties. Indeed, the experiments that he could conduct
were "such, and so numerous, that neither my energies nor
my income (even were that income a thousand times larger
than it is) could suffice for making all the required observations."

Rejecting that ideal of the "contribution of many wits"
as espoused by Bacon and which was to be taken up by
Leibniz, Descartes forcefully rejected the very idea of an
intellectual collaboration: "I can say, I think, without vanity, that if there is anyone capable of completing them [his
works], that person should be none other than myself."[16] In
contrast, one is of necessity reminded of Bacon's assertion:
"And indeed I exert myself in behalf of those things to the
hazard of others. . . . I am not hunting for fame, nor do I
take pleasure in finding a sect, after the fashion of heresi-
archs. . . . We ask that men themselves take part in the
labors that remain to be done." Descartes had no need of
other minds; any volunteers would cause him only to lose
valuable time. All he wanted was enough money to pay for
the employment of those who would carry out work under
his direction; his real wish was to be liberated from every
economic worry and every needless waste of time.[17]

---

[15]*Ibid.*, p. 156.
[16]*Ibid.*
[17]"As regards the observations which can be helpful it is true
that one man is not equal to making all of them. But the only
hands that he can usefully employ besides his own are those of
artisans or people of the kind whom he can pay and who may be
induced by hope of gain (a very efficient incentive) to carry out
accurately all the directions he might give them. For as to those

In the light of these considerations, the passage in the *Discourse on Method,* so frequently cited by the proponents of Cartesian "humanism," for whom the image of a knowledge progressively growing in the course of time appears once more conjoined to the ideal of collaboration between investigators, also acquires a precise meaning.

Descartes' best remedy against life's brevity and the lack of experiments was expressed in the hope "to make known the treatise I had written, showing so convincingly the advantage which would thereupon accrue to the public," so that "those who follow will be enabled to begin where their predecessors have left off. By thus uniting the lives and labors of many, we should collectively advance much further than each by himself could do."[18]

By isolating these utterances from the context of the *Discourse on Method,* Descartes has been explained as a proponent of collaboration between scientists and as a theoretician of progress. But matters stand quite differently. The rigidly deductive ideal of Cartesian science and Descartes' attempt to anchor physics solidly in metaphysics were not without effect on the very formulation of the concept of the progressive character of knowledge. In the *Principia,* his argument was not for the successive "discovery" of new truth, but for the deduction and passage from universally valid principles to other truths derived or deduced from

---

who, whether from curiosity or a desire to learn, may perchance of their own accord come forward to assist him, not only are they wont to make many promises which they do not fulfill but invariably they require to be repaid by help in several of their difficulties, or, at least, by compliments and interviews so useless that all time spent in them is lost. . . . Accordingly, if there were anywhere in the world someone whom he knew capable of making discoveries of supreme importance and of the greatest possible ability to the public; and if all other men were eager to assist him by every means in their power, yet I do not see how they could do anything for him beyond contributing to the expenses of the observations he would require to have made; and for the rest seeing to it that he is not deprived of his leisure by any personal importunities." *Ibid.,* pp. 159–60.

[18]*Ibid.,* p. 151.

them. Once again the comparison with Bacon can be very illuminating. The great Chancellor had placed emphasis on the "vital spirit" present in the mechanical arts and in the idea that they are perfected by the course of time "who is the author of authors . . . for rightly is truth called the daughter of time, not of authority." Descartes, instead, placed the accent on the nucleus of *truth* present in the arts even when, in their beginnings, they were rude and imperfect. Bacon had militantly opposed the mechanical arts "founded on nature and the light of experience"—resulting from the contribution of "many wits and industries" and therefore capable of progress—to the barrenness of philosophy and intellectual sciences "worshiped and celebrated" like statues.[19] The Cartesian position was quite different from this: indeed it was very far from Bacon's intentions and also from those aims which motivated Leibniz:

For just as the arts, though in their beginnings they are rude and imperfect, are yet gradually perfected by practice, so in philosophy, when we have true principles we cannot fail by following them to meet sometimes with other truths; and we could not better prove the falsity of those of Aristotle than by saying that men made no progress in knowledge by their use during the many ages that prosecuted them.[20]

By comparing the "arts" and "philosophy," and by placing them on the same plane in the name of a deductive knowledge, Descartes was actually destroying the meaning of the Baconian opposition between them and the polemic flowing therefrom. For him the sterility of Aristotelianism stemmed from the *falsity* of Aristotelian philosophy. Pascal's contention that one could assert the contrary to what the ancients maintained without thereby contradicting them, is devoid of meaning in the context of Cartesian philosophy. For that matter, neither would a historical diagnosis of the limits

[19]F. Bacon, *Works* (London, 1857–1874), I, 475–58; III, 289–90.
[20]*Principia,* in *Oeuvres,* vol. IX, pp. 18–19.

and insufficiencies of the philosophies of the past based (as in Bacon) on the demonstration of the characteristic limits of a civilization have meaning in this type of philosophy. By rejecting the notion that the mechanical arts and philosophy were in opposition, Descartes also deprived of meaning that idea of progress which had drawn vital sustenance from that opposition.

3.

If we can believe Baillet, in the last years of his life Descartes had been working on the idea of opening a great school of arts and trades, the purpose of which was to establish real contacts between the work of scientists and that of artisans and technicians:

According to his plans several large halls were to be constructed in the Collège Royal and in other places open to the public. One particular room was to be set aside for each group of trades, and to each room was to be added a scientific laboratory equipped with all the mechanical instruments necessary or useful to the arts which were to be taught there. Sufficient funds would have to be raised not only for the expenses required by the experiments, but also for the remuneration of masters or teachers, whose number would be equal to that of the arts taught. These teachers were to be experts in mathematics and physics, so that they could answer all the artisans' questions, give them a reason for everything, and prepare them for the ultimate goal of making new discoveries in the arts.[21]

Descartes was convinced that the real progress of science hinged on the work of theorists. Technics, as such, does not contribute to the progress of scientific knowledge.

The awareness that "true physics" was closely connected with the *Gentilles inventions* of engineers and technicians was much greater in Mersenne and Gassendi than in Descartes. Both Mersenne and Gassendi rejected as dogmatic

---

[21]Baillet, *La vie de M. Des-Cartes* (Paris, 1691), vol. II, p. 434. The text is in *Oeuvres*, ed. Adam and Tannery, vol. XI, pp. 659–60.

the grandiose Cartesian attempt to create a demonstrative physics based on universal principles. For Mersenne the constituent and characteristic elements of the new science were the knowledge of phenomena and the practice of the mechanical arts.[22] On the one hand he upheld the opportunity to renounce essences, and to relegate the discussion on matter and form, on atoms and subtle matter, to the realm of unverifiable speculations; on the other hand, in opposition to the opinion of the ancients, he defended the dignity of the arts and insisted on the value of the practical applications of science. In his *Questions harmoniques* (1634) Mersenne wrote that it is not a degradation for the sciences, as Pythagoras and Plato contended, to become "sensible and mechanical"; on the contrary, God wills that the arts and sciences be "put into practice." Every science has been given to us by God, and this gift has not been granted "for the sole joy of the mind of the theorist" but so that every science may be exercised "with the end of the utility of others in view and for the honor of Him who is its first and sovereign author." Through the arts, Mersenne continued, man places himself in a position "to construct a statics, hydraulics, and pneumatics" and to "produce results so prodigious as to make it seem that men can imitate the most admirable works of God." Through them it should be possible "to move bodies of every type, . . . to build a bridge without pillars, to represent the course of the planets or the stars in a small sphere."[23]

In a polemic directed against the sterile knowledge of the dialecticians, Gassendi, for his part, contrasted the knowledge of empiricists and artisans to the pseudoscience of the metaphysicians:

[22]R. Lenoble, *Mersenne et la naissance du mécanisme* (Paris, 1943), pp. 534-35.
[23]M. Mersenne, *Questions harmoniques* (Paris, 1634), p. 9; *La verité des sciences* (Paris, 1625), pp. 893, and the final part of the Preface.

How useful it would be to know the history of stones, metals, minerals, animals, and other things of this type of which there exists such a great variety pleasing to knowledge! But these things, it is objected, are known by stonecutters, goldsmiths, herbalists, and hunters. Philosophers, on the other hand, do not have the least consideration for these too vulgar things, while they boast of reserving their cogitations only for things that properly appertain to philosophy. But do you really think that Aristotle, Democritus, and the other great thinkers whose knowledge is so greatly esteemed did not cultivate philosophy while they were conducting investigations on these matters? And these good persons who neglect them, is it really true that they have a greater deference for philosophy when they doggedly discuss whether the form of corporeality is to be given to that form that is called the form of the cadaver, or what type of attribute such form possesses?[24]

Gassendi really was fighting to establish a new point of convergence between the knowledge of the empiricists and that of the philosophers. The new task that he assigned to reason (as has been trenchantly observed) was that of an "historical," phenomenal knowledge of the world of nature and of the human world.[25] For him, knowledge of the particular, and its organization according to quantitative and mechanical laws, as well as the elaboration of probable hypotheses, constituted the only valid form of knowledge. The abandonment of the dialectic as the typical instrument of metaphysical knowledge corresponded to the abandonment of a deductive and necessary science of essences. Gassendi repeated his appeal to the criterion of the utility of knowledge and to the mechanical arts as opposed to the use of the dialectic. What merchant or chemist or politician, he wondered in the *Exercitationes,* has ever made use of the dialectic? "It is clear that if I desire to know the truth of some things, I must turn to those arts and those sciences

[24]P. Gassendi, *Exercitationes paradoxicae adversus Aristoteleos,* in *Opera omnia* (Lugduni, 1658), vol. III, p. 107B.
[25]T. Gregory, *Scetticismo ed empirismo: studio su Gassendi* (Bari, 1961), pp. 127, 178.

that treat *ex professo* of these things, not to dialectics. Just as each science has its proper truth to know, so does it have its proper, specific rules of that knowledge."[26]

4.

It is in Galileo that we find for the first time the full convergence of the two traditions: the one based on the experimentation and practices of artisans and technicians, and the other based on the great corpus of theory and methodology of European science. The entrenchment of the theory of mechanical practice, as has already been noted by Leonard Olschki, and its transformation into science was the work of Galileo: empirical mechanics and the science of motion were fused into a solid whole of theoretical knowledge.

It would be pointless to dwell on the obvious and to quote from well-known texts if a distorted image of a rationalist and purely mathematical Galileo, remote from the knowledge of technicians and experimentalists—indeed assertively averse to it—had not been circulated and widely spread, even quite recently. For this reason it will be useful, first of all, to recall the celebrated beginning of the *Dialogues Concerning Two New Sciences*. Here we not only find the thesis that "investigation" *(filosofare)* must take into careful consideration the work of technicians and bear on the "activity" *(pratica)* of artisans, but also find explicit the recognition that the work of master craftsmen, described as "highly expert and clever in explanation" and in whom is accumulated the experience of generations, constitutes a help to the investigation carried on by "studious minds":

SALVIATI: The constant activity which you Venetians display in your famous arsenal suggests to the studious mind a large field for investigation, especially that part of the work which involves mechanics; for in this department all types of instru-

[26]Gassendi, *Exercitationes*, in *Opera omnia*, III, p. 152AB.

ments and machines are constantly being constructed by many artisans, among whom there must be some who, partly by whatever experience and partly by their own observations, have become highly expert and clever in explanation.

SAGREDO: You are quite right. Indeed, I myself, being curious by nature, frequently visit this place for the mere pleasure of observing the work of those who, on account of their superiority over other artisans, we call "first rank men." Consultation with them has often helped me in the investigation of certain effects including not only those which are striking, but also those which are recondite and almost incredible.[27]

Galileo was certainly keenly aware of the fact that the elevation of a theory shifts to another level, or, as he said, "far outweighs" the testimony and the observations of empiricists and technicians. The difference between knowledge (the cognition of the truth of a fact) and understanding "why this happens" is made evident by example in the section of the *Dialogues concerning Two New Sciences* dealing with the motion of projectiles:

SAGREDO: The force of rigid demonstration such as occurs only in mathematics fills me with wonder and delight. From accounts given by gunners, I was already aware of the fact that in the use of cannon and mortars the maximum range, that is the one in which the shot goes farthest, is obtained when the elevation is 45° or, as they say, at the sixth point of the quadrant. But to understand why this differs far outweighs the mere information obtained by the testimony of others or even by repeated experiment.

SALVIATI: What you say is very true. The knowledge of a single fact acquired through a discovery of its causes prepares the mind to understand and ascertain other facts without need of recourse to experiment, precisely as in the present case.[28]

Here the function of so-called theoretical models in the realm of scientific knowledge was explicitly proposed and

[27]G. Galilei, *Dialogues concerning Two New Sciences*, tr. Henry Crew and Alfonso de Salvio (Evanston, 1950), p. 1; cf. G. Galilei, *Opere* (Florence, 1890–1909), vol. VIII, p. 49.

[28]Galilei, *Dialogues concerning Two New Sciences*, pp. 264–65.

recognized. For science, a *fact* is only that which is arrived at on the basis of precise criteria of a theoretical character. In some cases the interpretation of the data of the experiment can occur on the basis of pre-established theses. In other words, some theses are placed at the base of those results of the experiment that "are removed" from them. The latter are interpreted as "disturbing circumstances." Here is an example of this mode of procedure:

I reason *ex suppositione:* suppose there is an object that moves toward a point that starts from a position of rest and accelerates, increasing in velocity proportionately to the increase in time. In this way I will conclusively demonstrate many accidents; then I add that if the experiment should show that such accidents were to be found verified in the motion of naturally descending weights, we could without error affirm that this is the same motion that I defined and supposed. If not, my demonstrations constructed upon my supposition would lose nothing of their efficacy and conclusiveness; just as nothing prejudices the conclusions that were drawn by Archimedes respecting the spiral, in that in nature there is no mobile object that moves spirally in that manner.[29]

The Galilean, Torricelli, was even more explicit:

I imagine and suppose that some body is moving downward and upward according to a known proportion, and horizontally with uniform motion. Given this, I say that everything that Galileo and that I, too, have said will follow. If then balls of lead, iron, or stone do not observe that supposed direction . . . we will say that we are not speaking of them.[30]

These aspects, on which we have deemed it important to dwell here, are fundamental to the Galilean methodology. They cannot simply be passed over in silence in order to defend, in accordance with Koyré, the portrait of an anti-Platonist and empiricist Galileo.[31] Neither is it possible to

[29]*Opere*, vol. VII, p. 156. Cf. E. May, *Elementi di filosofia della scienza* (Milan, 1951), pp. 63–64.
[30]See May, *Elementi di filosofia della scienza*, p. 64.
[31]Cf. A. Koyré, *Etudes Galiléenes* (Paris, 1939–1940), III; "Galileo e Platone," *Atti della fondazione G. Ronchi*, VIII:2 (1953), re-

transform what was a very firm Galilean faith in a world objectively structured according to the laws of mathematics and written in geometric characters, into a form of instrumentalism.[32] The disclosure of the great debt that Galileo owed to so-called Platonism certainly does not authorize us to forget, or to place on a secondary plane as irrelevant episodes, the significance of Galileo's interest in the work of technicians, nor his passion for observation, measure, and drawing. The same holds true for his veneration of Archimedes, his construction of the geometric military compass, and the thermo-baroscope in his study in Padua, as well as his investigations of the resistance of materials and his innumerable letters dedicated to a discussion and analysis of problems connected with bridge and canal building, floods, ballistics, and fortifications. Nor should we forget that it is the Platonist Galileo who sought information from Spanish navigators and who asserted: "Histories, that is to say things experienced, are the principles upon which the sciences are built."

The significance and the revolutionary importance of Galileo's attitude toward technics and instruments become particularly evident when we refer to the position he assumed toward the telescope. Although fourteen years after its invention, Galileo asserted that he had invented it "by

printed in *Introduzione alla lettura di Platone* (Florence, 1956), pp. 207–41; *From the Closed World to the Infinite Universe* (Baltimore, 1957), pp. 72–76, 88–95; "Newton, Galilée et Platon," *Annales* (1960), pp. 1041–59. Many of the presuppositions from which Koyré starts out clearly come to light in his most recent and comprehensive work, *La révolution astronomique, Copernic, Kepler, Borelli* (Paris, 1961). For the polemic with Koyré see L. Geymonat, *Discorsi Galileo Galilei* (Turin, 1957), Preface; the Galilean anthology, *Sensate esperienze e certe dimostrazioni,* ed. F. Brunetti and L. Geymonat (Bari, 1961), esp. pp. 19, 247n.

[32]See also E. A. Burtt, *The Metaphysical Foundations of Modern Physical Science* (London, 1950), pp. 61ff., 309ff.; E. W. Strong, *Procedures and Metaphysics* (Berkeley, 1936); A. Banfi, *Galileo Galilei* (Milan, 1949), p. 271 and *passim;* E. Garin, "La filosofia," in *Storia dei generi letterari italiani* (Milan, 1947), pp. 287ff.; "La nuova scienza e il simbolo del libro," in *La cultura filosofica del Rinascimento italiano* (Florence, 1961), pp. 454ff.

way of discourse," it now has been sufficiently demonstrated that around 1609 he had had scanty preparation in optics and that the discovery "derived from experiment and not from mathematics."[33] What really counts, and marks a revolution in the attitude of the scientist, is Galileo's *trust* in an instrument produced in the ambience of the artisans —an instrument which had been gradually perfected "through practice" and was partially accepted in military circles but ignored, when not despised, by the official scientific establishment. Galileo's harsh opposition to bookish learning was born of this new attitude toward technico-artisan knowledge and the rejection of the centuries-old separation between speculative and empirical mechanics.

Physics no longer constituted an exercise "in what it is possible to do in a particular sector of philosophy"; method was not an "end in itself"; and experimental investigations were not isolated examples of "everyday observations" without effect on general doctrines. The investigation of the problems of motion and weight entailed the attentive and direct study of the procedures used by mechanics working in the arsenals, cannoneers, and engineers for the purpose of lifting weights, launching projectiles, and draining marsh lands.

It was no accident that the men of the seventeenth century who were interested in a history of the arts, in an accurate description of the techniques of the transformation of nature, were to see in Galileo one of the founders of the new "experimental philosophy."

5.

The limits of the Baconian method derive, no doubt, from an insufficient appraisal of the function performed, in the realm of scientific cognition, by hypotheses, by the "anticipation of the experiment," and by axiomatic systems of a

[33]Cf. V. Ronchi, *Galileo e il cannochiale* (Udine, 1942), pp. 179ff.; Geymonat, *Galileo Galilei*, p. 70ff.

deductive character. The typically Platonic images of a world of mathematical and rational structures created by a geometer God who composed the world out of *numero, pondere, et mensura* doubtlessly were to be more fruitful to the development of modern science than the Baconian image of nature as a "forest" and a "labyrinth." The so-called Baconian "incomprehension" of mathematics which led Bacon to appreciate "mechanics" such as Agricola more than "theorists" such as Copernicus and Galileo was deeply bound up with his appraisal of logic as a "labyrinthian thread" as a means for ordering the natural forest.

In Galileo and even in Newton, both of whom were so strongly tied to many Baconian positions, we find a forceful reaffirmation of that principle which Bacon had relegated to the margins of his theory of reality, namely, that of the simplicity, economy, and inexorableness of nature. It was precisely in the area of "Platonic" formulation and affirmation of the simplicity of nature (which recurs also in the first of the four Newtonian *regulae*) that a type of interrogation of natural reality was arrived at which was very different from Bacon's, and which functioned, as I have tried to demonstrate elsewhere, on the basis of models derived from the tradition of rhetoric.[34]

The founders of the Royal Society, the authors of the great Enlightenment encyclopedias, and not a few positivist historians and philosophers of the nineteenth century, were fond of the portrait of Bacon as the "father of modern science" because of his discovery of the inductive method. But to still consider Bacon from this point of view would be tantamount, as Benjamin Farrington has trenchantly observed, to placing him on an inappropriate pedestal in an inappropriate part of the gallery.

Nevertheless, the fact remains that when Bacon turned to the mechanical arts, considering them capable of revealing the actual processes of nature, and saw in them that

[34]Cf. Rossi, *Francis Bacon.*

capacity to give rise to inventions and works absent in the traditional knowledge—when polemicising against the logic of the schools, he projected a history of the arts and of technics as an indispensable prerequisite to a reform of learning—he truly became the spokesman for some fundamental demands of the culture of his time. Bacon brought to full awareness some of the thematic ideas that had been making slow headway at the margins of the official science in that world of technicians, engineers, and builders to which men like Biringuccio and Agricola had belonged. On one hand, these Baconian theses were to be appealed to by the proponents of "experimental philosophy" gathered around the Royal Society, on the other by scientists and philosophers, such as Boyle and Leibniz.

The project of a history of mechanics, or history of the arts, was formulated for the first time in the *Advancement of Learning* (1605) and then taken up again on a much larger scale, and more forcefully, in the *Parasceve ad historiam naturalem et experimentalem* (published in 1620 as an appendix to the *Novum organum*) and finally in *De dignitate et augmentis scientiarium* in 1623. The history of the arts, affirms Bacon, up to now has been considered in a way so wretched and useless that it must be placed among the *desiderata* of the new encyclopedia of the sciences:

I find some collections made of agricultural and likewise of many manual arts; but always (which is of great detriment in this kind of learning) with a neglect and a rejection of experiments familiar and vulgar; which yet in the interpretation of nature are of equal, if not of more value than those which are less common. [It is deemed a dishonor] . . . to education for learned men to descend to inquiry or meditations upon matters mechanical. . . . But, if my judgment be of any weight, the use of History Mechanical is, of all others, the most radical and fundamental towards natural philosophy.

The task to be assigned to a history of the arts was of a twofold character: "For it will not be of only immediate benefit, by converting and transferring the observations of one art to the use of others. . . . But further it would give a more true and real illumination concerning the investigation of the causes of things and axioms of arts."[35]

It is known that Bacon, near the end of his life, subordinated the very project of a new logic to the history of free nature and the history of mechanics, that is, the history of nature modified by the hand of man.[36] In the *Parasceve*, Bacon insisted, with particular efficacy, on the importance of a history of artisan techniques. He argued that even if all the great minds of all ages should gather in assembly, even if all men were to dedicate themselves to the study of philosophy, and even if the world were to be filled with academies and colleges, no progress would be possible without a natural and experimental history. Such a history appeared to him as a work of vast scope (*res magnae molis*), an "almost royal" enterprise which could not be brought to completion without great cost and toil.[37] Bacon devoted much space to the mechanical arts in his catalogue, which included one hundred and thirty particular histories. Such histories he asserted "exhibit things in motion and lead more directly to practice," and through them "man can remove the mask and veil from natural objects." Here, Bacon continued, it is expedient that "all fineness and daintiness" be set aside so that efforts could be concentrated upon this history, . . . mechanical and ill bred as it may seem." The techniques which could be most fruitfully studied, according to Bacon, are those which alter and transform material objects such as "agriculture, cookery, chemistry, dyeing, the manufacture of glass, enamel, sugar, gunpowder, artificial fires, paper and the like."[38] Not to

---

[35]Bacon, *Works*, I, 497, 499–500 (*De augmentis*); III, 332–33 (*Advancement*).

[36]For the thesis of the superiority of natural history over the doctrine of method, *Novum organum*, I, 130; *Works*, II, 16 (*Auctoris monitum*).

[37]Bacon, *Works*, I, 393–94 (*Parasceve*); *Novum organum*, I, 130.

[38]Bacon, *Works*, I, 399–400 (*Parasceve*).

be neglected, even if they are of lesser utility, were those arts which "consist principally in the subtle motion of the hands of instruments . . . such as weaving, carpentry, architecture, the manufacture of clocks and the like." Bacon had expressed himself no less differently on a page of his *Diary* written in 1608: for the purpose of compiling a mechanical history, he had planned to conduct investigations on the materials used in the arts, on the instruments and machines used by artisans and technicians, on the mode of application and use of every instrument, on the mistakes that technicians could possibly commit because of the isolation of their specific art, and finally on the possible modes of perfecting and improving the techniques of manufacture and processing.[39] For Bacon the progress of science and the improvement of the human condition required that the knowledge of technicians be integrated into the fields of science and natural philosophy, from which for centuries it had been sealed off by tradition. The methods, procedures, operations, and language of the mechanical arts had made headway and had been perfected outside the official science in a world of engineers, architects, skilled artisans, builders of machines, and instruments. Those methods, procedures, and languages, he argued, now had to become the object of consideration, reflection, and study. And it was not only a question of once and for all giving up inveterate prejudices against "mechanical things" by a lone intellectual. The ends to which Bacon pointed were much broader and much less personal: the academies, colleges, scientific societies, sovereigns, and states must place themselves at the head of this movement of renewal. Only along this path, with the help of these great organizations, argues Bacon, will the *experientia erratica* of the mechanics, the tangle of the investigations and observations made by the artisans, and the daily labors of those who transform nature through the

---

[39]James Spedding, ed. and comp. *The Letters and Life of Francis Bacon, Including All his Occasional Works*, 7 vols. (London: Longmans, Green, Reader and Dyer, 1861–1872), IV, pp. 65–66 (*Commentarius solutus*).

work of their hands be removed from chance and the ambiguous temptations of magic to give rise to a grandiose organic and systematic *corpus* of knowledge. Only along this path will it be possible to make the world and the type of society described in *The New Atlantis* a reality.

6.

Different groups of intellectuals in England, after 1640, worked for the realization of this grandiose Baconian project. One of these groups, which had Robert Boyle among its leaders, sprang into being from an encounter between future members of the so-called Philosophical College:

About the year 1645, while I lived in London (at a time, when, by our Civil Wars, academical studies were much interrupted in both universities) . . . I had opportunity of being acquainted with diverse worthy persons, inquisitive into Natural Philosophy and other parts of human Learning, [a]nd particularly of what hath been called the New Philosophy or Experimental Philosophy. . . . Our business was (precluding matters of theology and state-affairs) . . . to discourse of the circulation of blood, the valves in the veins, . . . the Copernican hypothesis, the nature of comets and the new stars, the satellites of Jupiter, . . . the weight of air, the possibility or impossibility of vacuities . . . Some were then but New Discoveries, and others not so generally known and embraced as now they are, with others appertaining to what hath been called the New Philosophy which from the times of Galileo at Florence, and Sir Francis Bacon in England, hath been much cultivated in Italy, France, Germany and other parts abroad, as well as with us in England.[40]

The Royal Society was born from these meetings which, in a second phase, took place at Oxford. Among its first projects was that of making "faithful records of all the works of nature, or art" and to study, through the work of apposite commissions, "the probable effects of experiments,

[40]On the characteristics of these groups, see W. E. Houghton, "The History of Trades," in Wiener and Noland, eds., *Roots of Scientific Thought*, p. 360.

in respect of all the manual trades."[41] Thomas Sprat, pushing the Baconian position to the extreme (Bacon certainly would not have sustained the thesis that scientific research should be subordinated to ends proper to the mechanical arts), asserted: "What visible benefit did ancient philosophy ever bring? The ancient mechanicks and artificers—to whom the true natural philosophy should have been principally directed—were very far from being helped in any way by those abstruse doctrines." On the other hand, all members of the Society were requested to adopt "a close, naked natural way of speaking; positive expressions; clear senses; a native easiness, bringing all things as near the mathematical clarity as they can: and preferring the language of artisans, countrymen, and merchants, before that of wits or scholars."[42]

But already in the years between Bacon's death (1626) and the foundation of the Royal Society (1663), researchers and reformers such as Samuel Hartlib, John Drury, William Petty, and John Evelyn seemed to be greatly interested in the problem of the betterment of society and inventions. In their work Bacon's influence and the universalistic aspirations of Comenius were closely associated with motives of an economical and commercial character.[43] In Hartlib's utopia, "Solomon's House" as described in *The New Atlantis* undergoes a radical transformation: five "councils of state" that are responsible for the administration of public affairs have tasks of a predominantly industrial and commercial character.[44]

The English *virtuosi* of the seventeenth century were the expression of a society that saw its well-being rapidly increase in consequence of the rapid improvements of technics. They had a very keen passion for science and for the

[41]T. Sprat, *History of the Royal Society* (London, 1734), pp. 61, 378–403.
[42]*Ibid.*, p. 113.
[43]W. E. Houghton, "The History of Trades," pp. 360–61.
[44]S. Hartlib, *A Description of the Famous Kingdom of Macaria* (London, 1641).

study of nature, but the "advancement of learning" signified progress in technics and accumulation of riches. John Drury wrote: "As regards invention and industries, I will look principally for those which effect the advance of knowledge . . . and which are useful to the preservation and the increase of wealth through the trades and the mechanical industries, whether practiced on land or sea, for peace or war."[45] John Wilkins, glorifying the function of mathematics and of natural philosophy, addressed a clearly defined public:

In my philosophical and mathematical investigations, in addition to the happiness and pleasure which they procure, there is also the possibility of a real benefit of a practical character: in particular for those gentlemen who risk their patrimony in those vexatious and costly adventures such as the extraction of coal . . . and also for those artificers who are skillful in the practice of these arts.[46]

In the project of a *gymnasium mechanicum* or "college of artisans for the progress of all the mechanical arts and of the manufactures" advanced by William Petty in 1648, there are all the elements that characterize experimental philosophy: the polemic against an exclusively bookish culture; the reaffirmation of the indivisibility of technics and science and of the practical and utilitarian ends of science; the project of a complete history of the arts; and the hope in a marvelous flowering of inventions and discoveries. Among the books to be included in the *gymnasium mechanicum,*

we recommend in the first place the compilation of a work which could have as a title: *Velleus aurum, sive facultatum luciferarum descriptio magna.* In them should be extensively

[45] J. Dury, *The Purpose and Platform of My Journey into Germany* (1631): the text (from ms Sloane 654 of the British Museum) is published in G. H. Turnbull, *Samuel Hartlib* (London, 1920), p. 11.
[46] J. Wilkins, *Mathematical and Philosophical Works* (London, 1802), p. 128.

set forth all the means employed by men in view of their subsistence and through which they construct their fortunes. . . . In the history of arts should be described the entire process of manual operations and of the applications of a natural thing to others through the necessary instruments and machines. . . . In this work bare words are not sufficient: all the tools and instruments should be painted and colored inasmuch as description, without colors, would turn out to be insufficient. . . . Young men, instead of reading difficult Hebrew words in the Bible, . . . or repeating like parrots nouns or irregular verbs, will be able to read and learn the history of human faculties . . . and it could be more useful for youths to spend ten or twenty years in the study of things and of this book, rather than in that heap of words. . . . From this work must needs derive a great progress of useful and honorable inventions since a man, at a glance, will be able to embrace all the work carried out by our predecessors and consequently be in a position to remedy all the deficiencies of an individual trade with the perfections of another.[47]

These projects reflected aspirations that were very widespread. In the college projected by Abraham Cowley in 1664, the students were to study "the mysteries of all the arts and their advancements, the fabrication of all products . . . in short all the things contained in the Catalogue of natural histories annexed to the *organum* of Lord Bacon."[48]

In a letter to Wotton, dated March 30, 1696, John Evelyn stated that he had found Robert Boyle's library to be very small. He described it as that of a man who "has learned more from men than from books, from experiments and from his laboratory which instead is ample and well furnished."[49] The enthusiasm for technics and for the

[47]*The Advice of William Petty to Mr. Samuel Hartlib for the Advancement of some particular Parts of Learning* (1648), in *The Hartleian Miscellany* (1808–1811), VI, pp. 146, 152–53, 155.

[48]A. Cowley, *Proposition for the Advancement of Learning*, in A. B. Gough, ed., *Essays and other Prose Writings* (London, 1915), p. 34.

[49]*Diary of J. Evelyn to which are added a Selection from his Familiar Letters* (London, 1879), vol. III, p. 485.

mechanical arts exhibited by men such as Evelyn, Petty, and Boyle was closely connected with the polemic—a lively issue in their ambience—against the traditional bookish culture imparted in the schools: this is the source of the opposition we find in them between the "scientist" and "experimenter" and the "learned man" who was formed exclusively from books.

"The studies to which I apply myself," wrote Boyle to Marcomber in October, 1646, "are natural philosophy, mechanics, and agriculture, in keeping with the principles of our new philosophical college which values knowledge only if it is useful to practice."[50] In 1671 he wrote that he had learned more about stones from two or three stonecutters than he had ever learned from reading Pliny, Aristotle, and all their commentators.[51] In another letter, undated, to Clodius, he affirmed that in the books which he had read in the course of his life, he never saw reflected that variety and those subtle expedients of nature which, instead, he had perceived while dissecting animals.[52]

Boyle—in a polemic which on more than one point approached a sort of "scientific primitivism"—often opposed the book of nature, the artisan's workshop, the anatomical room in opposition to libraries, the studies of men of letters and humanists, and to investigations of a purely theoretical character. In the *Considerations touching the Usefulness of Experimental Natural Philosophy* published in 1671,[53] Boyle gave a coherent and finished form to this trend of thought and to the interests and aspirations of the Baconian groups operating in seventeenth-century England. In these pages we again come upon Bacon's polemic against the indifference of the men of culture to the work of illiterate mechanics, the assertion of the necessity of compiling a history of nature modified by work, and finally the thesis

[50]R. Boyle, *Works,* ed. Birch (London, 1744), I, p. 20.
[51]*Ibid.,* III, p. 444.
[52]*Ibid.,* IV, p. 55.
[53]See *ibid.,* III, pp. 442–56.

that the procedures of technics are of a greater utility than the reading of the classics for an actual knowledge of the natural world.

> 'Tis a prejudice no less pernicious than general, which natural philosophy, and the interest of mankind receive, that learned and ingenious persons should have been kept strangers to the shop and practices of tradesmen. . . . Most of the phenomena that arise in trade, are part of a natural history; and therefore, demand the naturalist's care. . . . They show us nature in motion, and that too when turn'd out of her course by human power, which is a most instructive state wherein we can behold her.[54]

The experiments conducted by the "virtuosi" in their laboratories, continues Boyle, have the merit of a notable accuracy of observation, but, in the experiments conducted in artisan workshops, the shortcomings of lessened accuracy are compensated for by greater diligence in every experiment, for each time the artisan stakes his very means of subsistence, and the observations "are repeated with greater frequency and conducted with greater assiduousness than occurs through the experiments with which men of culture have enriched natural history." In the technical workshop, objects are at once examined and modified "by mechanical way": this type of "mechanical" procedure, which the "bookman" considers irrelevant, can turn out to be "true" and stimulate the advancement of useful knowledge.

In order to avoid the confinement of this knowledge to the margins of culture and science, and in order to effect a fruitful exchange between the procedures employed in the various sectors of technics, Boyle considered it to be a matter of prime necessity that a group of scholars devote itself to the collection of the material requisite for the compilation of a vast history of the arts. The fourth essay in the

[54]P. Shaw, *Works of Boyle Abridged* (London, 1725), pp. 129–30.

Considerations bears a significant title: "That the Goods of Mankind may be much increased by the Naturalist's Insight into Trades." Here Boyle was reproposing to the culture of the late seventeenth century the program which had been originally formulated by Francis Bacon at the beginning of the same century.[55]

That *Verulamian design,* which one of Boyle's correspondents had discussed,[56] had taken on an even greater importance on the institutional plane. In 1664 a resolution of the Royal Society petitioned the king "that he instruct the two Secretaries of State that all proposals concerning mechanical inventions be submitted to the Council of the Society and be examined by the latter to see if they were new, true, useful." The petition was not granted, but a week later the Society organized itself into eight commissions: among these were the "georgic," or agricultural commission, of 32 members; the mechanical, 67; and the commission for the history and description of trades, 35. Two years later, in France, the *Académie des Sciences* (founded by Louis XIV a few years after the establishment of the Royal Society) created a commission which was assigned the task of examining the work methods of artisans and technicians, and of studying defects of their instruments. One of the members of the Academy, Perrault, published a famous collection of illustrations and descriptions of all the

[55]On the English "Virtuosi," see W. E. Houghton, "The English Virtuoso in the XVIIth Century," *Journal of the History of Ideas* (1942), pp. 51–73, 190–219; P. Allen, "Scientific Studies in the English Universities in the XVIIth Century," *Journal of the History of Ideas* (1949). On Boyle's work as a disseminator of scientific knowledge, see J. F. Fulton, "Robert Boyle and his Influence in the XVIIth Century," *Isis* (1932), pp. 77–102; on Boyle as scientist, L. T. More, "Robert Boyle as Alchemist," *Journal of the History of Ideas* (1941), pp. 61–67; *The Life and Works of Robert Boyle* (London, 1944); M. Boas, *Robert Boyle and Seventeenth-Century Chemistry* (Cambridge, 1958).

[56]Letter written by John Beale, July 13, 1666, in Boyle, *Works,* ed. Birch, p. 478.

machines which had been submitted to the judgment of the Academy and approved by it.[57]

In 1675 Colbert asked the members of the Academy to prepare a *summa* of the technical knowledge of the age. His request originated from the problems inherent in his grandiose policy of industrial mercantilism. But the first volume, dedicated to the art of printing, did not appear until 1704, and the publication of the volumes of illustrations was suspended, probably because of the appearance of Diderot's *Encyclopédie*.[58]

7.

One of the most widely circulated works of seventeenth-century European culture was the *Encyclopedia* prepared by Henry Alsted and published in Herborn in 1630 and subsequently reprinted many times. From this work we can get an idea of the deep inroads which the appraisal of the mechanical arts, present in the writings of not a few great exponents of European culture, had made into even the official and university culture. In Alsted's work, the type of "defense" of the mechanical arts that we have found in Vives, Palissy, Biringuccio, and Agricola underwent a reversal that was indicative of the extreme diversity of situations. To defend the art of metalworking from the accusation of "unworthiness," Agricola had referred to times when architecture and medicine had been practiced by slaves; but, he argued, architecture and medicine were not to be considered occupations unworthy of a free man for this reason. Alsted, however, was able to refer to a very different situation. The mechanical arts were not to be considered unworthy, because in his time men of great culture

[57]Cf. G. N. Clark, *Science and Social Welfare in the Age of Newton* (Oxford, 1949), p. 18; P. Gauja, *L'Académie des sciences* (Paris, 1934).

[58]B. Gille, "L'encyclopédie, dictionnaire technique," in *L'encyclopédie et le progrès des sciences et des techniques* (Paris, 1952), p. 188.

had toiled in the mechanical arts and had worked on behalf of knowledge and its advancement. Even more significant was the attempt, present in Alsted's treatment of the subject, to trace the very distinction between mechanical and liberal arts to a particular historical situation, disclosing the economic and social origin of the traditional condemnation of the mechanical arts: "They are in fact not called *illiberal* because they are such by their nature or character, but because the Greeks, who coined this term, allowed only free men to dedicate themselves to the liberal arts, and they excluded from them the slaves who were relegated to the mechanical arts."[59]

Leibniz recalled Alsted's work with admiration on several occasions. A brief essay in 1671[60] was devoted to an improvement and perfectioning of Alsted's *Encyclopedia*. But the Leibnizian ideal of peaceful coexistence between church and state, and of a common participation of all men in the progress of knowledge, derived not so much from Alsted's work and from the other Herborn encyclopediasts as from Leibniz's full and enthusiastic approval of Bacon's projects for the renewal of learning, and Comenius' pansophic universalism.[61]

[59]Joan Henrici Alstedii, *Scientiarum omnium Enciclopaediae* (Lugduni, 1649), p. 119. On Alsted: Carreras y Artau, *La filosofia cristiana* (Madrid, 1939–1943), vol. II, pp. 239–49; P. Rossi, *Clavis universalis arti mnemoniche e logica combinatoria da Lullo a Leibniz* (Milan, 1960), pp. 74–75, 179–84, 247; L. E. Loemker, "Leibniz and the Herborn Encyclopedists," *Journal of the History of Ideas* (1961), pp. 323–38.

[60]"Cogitata quaedam de ratione perficiendi et emendandi Encyclopaediam Alstedii," in L. Dutens, *G. G. Leibnitii Opera Omnia,* 6 vols. (Geneva, 1768), vol. V, p. 183. L. Couturat, *Opuscules et fragments inedits de Leibniz* (Paris, 1903), pp, 354–55. On his relations with Alsted see Loemker, "Leibniz and the Herborn Encyclopedists"; D. Mahnke, "Leibnizens Synthese von Universal-Mathematic und Individual-Metaphysik," *Jahrbuch fur Philos. und Phänomenologische Forschung* (1925), pp. 305–612; Rossi, *Clavis universalis,* pp. 237ff.

[61]For Leibniz's appraisal of Bacon's philosophy see the following passages: *Dissertatio de Arte Combinatoria,* in *Die Philosophischen Schrifften von G. W. Leibniz,* 7 vols., ed. C. I. Gerhardt (Berlin,

Leibniz expressed with great clarity the idea, already present in Bacon, of an *enlightenment* brought to theories by the work of technicians and mechanics, in a reference to the work of Galileo and Harvey:

If Galileo had not talked with the builders of water conduits and had not learned from other artisans that in a suction pump water cannot be raised higher than thirty feet, we would still not know the secret of the weight of air, the vacuum pump, and the barometer. By considering the ligatures of the surgeons who cut veins, Harvey for his part was the first to suspect the circulatory motion of the blood.[62]

1875–1890), vol. IV, p. 64; *Confessio naturae, ibid.,* vol. IV, p. 105; *Initia et specimina, ibid.,* vol. VII, p. 67, contains a judgment which merits rereading: "At cogitationum novitate ad splendore facile priores omnes (Vives, Ramo, etc.) vicit Franciscus Baconus Cancellarius Angliae edito pulcherrimo opere *De augmentis scientarum.* Sed viro summo defuisse otium et interiores literas, et denique mathematici rigoris amusim indicatu facile est; quae tamen omnia ingenii magnitudine compensabantur. Itaque dicere potuit quae facienda essent, ignoravit tamen saepe quae jam facta essent, deinde nimium tribuit philosophiae empiricae." In the autobiography *(In specimen placidii introductio historica)* Leibniz writes: "Intera felici re accidit ut consilia magni viri Francisci Baconi, Angliae Cancellarii, *De augmentis scientiarum* et cogitata excitatissma Cardani et Campanellae, et specimina melioris philosophiae Kepleri et Galilei et Cartesii ad manus pervenirent. Tum ille, ut postea amicis saepe praedicavit, velut in alium orbem delatus." In the *Dissertatio praeliminaris* to Nizolio's *De veris principiis et vera ratione philosphandi* (in *Schriften,* vol. IV, p. 143): "Antequam incomparabilis Verulamius aliique praeclari viri philosophiam ex aéris divagationibus aut etiam spatio imaginario ad terram hanc nostram et usum vitae revocarunt. . . ." Even more interesting is the comparison between the paired Bacon-Campanella and the paired Descartes-Hobbes made by Leibniz in his *Reflections: (Leibnitiana,* LIII, *Oeuvres,* ed. Dutens, vol. IV, p. 303) "Quid Cartesio in physicis, Hobbio in moralibus acutius? At si ille Bacono, hic Campanellae comparetur, apparet illos humi rapere. . . ."

For the relations with Comenius see Carreras y Artau, *La filosofia cristiana,* vol. II, p. 320; L. Couturat, *La logique de Leibniz d'après des documents inedits* (Paris, 1901), pp. 571–73; *Judicium de scriptis comenianis,* in Dutens, *Leibnitii Opera,* vol. V, pp. 181–82. On his relations with Bisterfield and with the Herborn circles, and on the presence of motifs drawn from the mystic-Pythagorean currents, see W. Kabitz, *Die Philosophie der jungen Leibniz. Untersuchungen zur Entwicklungsgeschichte seines Systems* (Heidelberg, 1909).

[62]*Philosophischen Schriften,* vol. VII, p. 69.

The above passage belongs to an essay whose very title betrays its Baconian inspiration: the *Initia e specimina scientiae novae generalis pro instauratione et augmentis scientiarium ad publicam felicitatem*. In technical knowledge, unlike what occurs in philosophy, "we do not pit ourselves against words but with things themselves"; nevertheless, the advances made in the mechanical arts are to a great extent still ignored by cultured men. On the one hand, technicians are in the dark as to the use that can be made of the results of their observations and experiments, on the other both scientists and technicians "do not know that their *desiderata* can be satisfied by the labor of mechanics." If the experiments and observations of technicians could be gathered in an organic *corpus* of knowledge, the human race—which is still unaware of its potentialities—would be astounded at its power. ("Perhaps we ourselves would marvel at our power, while now we heave sighs over our misery, unaware as we are of our faculties.")[63]

The program of a history of the arts was more energetically resumed in the *Discourse touching the method of Certitude and the Art of Invention*. The "unwritten cognitions" scattered among men who perform technical activities of sundry natures by far surpass all that which is found in books regarding quantity as well as importance ("*tant à l'égard de la multitude que de l'importance*"). The best part of the treasure of which the human race can avail itself has not yet been registered, writes Leibniz. Furthermore, there exists no mechanical art so small and "contemptible" that cannot offer observations and considerations of primary importance for science. Confronted with knowledge of a rhetorical type, and concerned only with vague discourses and sermons, the history of the practical activities of man appeared to Leibniz as a search directed toward real things which are advantageous for society:

Many learned men delight in vague and trite discourses, whereas there exists a vast terrain on which they would be

[63]*Ibid.*, pp. 69–70.

able to exercise their minds with solid and real things and advantageous to the masses. We are needful of a real "theatre of human life," taken from the practice of men, very different from that which has been handed down to us by some learned men in which, great as it is, there is only that which turns out to be useful only for the composition of harangues and sermons.

If only one of the arts were lost, continues Leibniz, all our libraries would not be able to remedy it. Therefore, he considered the task of committing to writing the procedures used by technicians and artisans as one of the most urgent tasks of the new culture. In his view such procedures, moreover, were perfectly describable insofar as practice is but a theory *"plus composé et particulière que la commune."*[64]

The Leibnizian project of a great encyclopedic inventory of the arts, born on the basis of a view of science and history, relied on the assertions of Bacon and was decisively opposed to the Cartesian attitude. Leibniz proposed a "republic of minds" in opposition to the solitude of Descartes and to his *"vanité de vouloir être solipse."*[65] A perusal of the *Discourse on Method* tends "to make us believe that Descartes had read very little, but, instead, employed his time in journeys and wars."[66] The real progress of the human race is born of the very past of science, and it is necessary to retest the ambition of those who despise others "as if, by themselves, they could do great things."[67] We must reject that sectarian spirit, Leibniz says, further alluding to Cartesianism which limits itself to the veneration of the teacher, for actually, "one man is a slight thing in comparison with the union of many men." The aim of philos-

[64]*Discours touchant la méthode de la certitude et l'art d'inventer pour finir les disputes et pour faire en peu de temps de grands progrès*, in *Die Philosophischen Schriften*, vol. VII, pp. 181–82.
[65]A. Foucher De Careil, *Nouvelles lettres et opuscules inédits de Leibniz* (Paris, 1875), p. 13.
[66]*Ibid.*, p. 18.
[67]*Philosophischen Schriften*, vol. VII, p. 128.

ophy is not that of the cultivation of one's own intellect but that of improving the intellect of all men:[68] the method must be integrally transmissible and communicable. The results which Descartes had derived depended instead "more on his genius than on his method," and the insufficiency of the method is reflected with particular evidence in the comportment of Cartesians who not only "study the writings of the master, rather than the book of nature," but are incapable of any invention or progress whatsoever precisely because they ignore others and deprive themselves of the advantages that derive from collaboration.[69]

In a passage that is obviously an allusion to the *Discourse on Method*, Leibniz insisted on the validity and significance of a nonfictitious collaboration. On this point he was violently "anti-Cartesian" and truly and profoundly "Baconian."

Instead of holding each other by the hand to guide ourselves reciprocally and to make surer our path, we run haphazardly. We also mire ourselves in the swamps and the shifting sands of doubts without end. . . . But in these dark shadows of life and in the midst of such great dangers, it is not up to any one mortal to light a torch capable of illuming this darkness. . . . We must walk together in concert, join our labors, abandon the spirit of the sects and the affection of novelty.[70]

For Leibniz, as for Pascal, the history of the world was comparable to the history of an individual, and the cognizing subject is the whole of mankind that operates in history.[71] The succession of individuals in time is not an inco-

---

[68]Cf. O. Klopp, *Die Werke von Leibniz*, 11 vols. (Hanover, 1864–1884), vol. X, p. 19; *Textes inédits de Leibniz publiés et annotés par G. Grua* (Paris, 1958), p. 578.

[69]*Philosophischen Schriften*, vol. II, p. 535; Foucher de Careil, *Nouvelles lettres*, p. 13.

[70]*Philosophischen Schriften*, vol. VII, pp. 157–59. The most comprehensive study of the relations between Descartes and Leibniz is found in the excellent book by Y. Beleval, *Leibniz critique de Descartes* (Paris, 1960).

[71]*Nova methodus*, paragraphs 7, 38.

herent juxtaposition of entities independent of each other. The knowledge of the human race is born of the collaboration between the living and the dead, as well as by men working together. It is not only secured in archives and libraries, but is actuated and takes shape in all the activities to which men dedicate themselves. For Leibniz, recourse must be had to all these activities: to the work of scientists and learned men, to the scattered observations of artisans and peasants, to musicians, theater people, sailors, merchants, including even horsemen, dancers, and charlatans.[72]

In these Leibnizian writings, the discussion on the mechanical arts gave rise to a new appraisal of human labor. The assertion of the relevancy of the work of technicians to the advancement of science and culture appeared closely linked to the universalist and historicist ideal of a knowledge that is born of the joint effort of generations and is the work of all peoples: *conjunctis in unum omnium temporum et gentium studiis.*[73]

8.

In the prefatory pages written by d'Alembert to the *Encyclopédie ou dictionnaire raisonné des sciences, des arts et des métiers,* there is an awareness that a great undertaking was bringing to maturation and fully actualizing a program of investigations which had precise historical origins. When the encyclopedists "addressed themselves to the artisans of France," they interrogated technicians and workers and then tried to define exactly the terms, methods, and procedures proper to the various arts in order to fit them into an organic and systematic *corpus* of knowledge. They projected a history of the arts and polemicized in favor of work on which light is continuously shed by knowledge of the theoretical principles which are its base. They were in favor of theoretical investigation capable of being adapted

---

[72]Klopp, *Die Werke von Leibniz*, vol. III, p. 323.
[73]*Philosophischen Schriften,* vol. VII, p. 130.

to practical application and of being reconverted into works. By so doing they were consciously putting themselves forward as the heirs and continuators of the program which had been staked out by Bacon. In the *Discours préliminaire*, d'Alembert wrote that in Chambers' *Cyclopedia* "we have found a prodigious multitude of lacunae in the sciences; in the liberal arts we found one word where pages were required; and in the mechanical arts everything needs to be started from scratch. Chambers has read books, but he has never seen artisans, and these are things that are learned only in the workshops."[74]

In the *Prospectus* of 1750 Diderot had expressed a similar dissatisfaction with the books in use up to that time and had made the same demand for the comprehension of those methods of work through direct observation which a long tradition had considered unworthy of attention:

We have turned to the most skilled workers of Paris and of all France, we have taken the trouble of going into their shops, in order to question them directly, and to commit to writing what they dictated to us, to develop their thoughts, to draw out from them the terms proper to their profession, to lay out panels, to define them, to converse with those from whom we had obtained memoirs and (an almost indispensable precaution) to rectify in long and frequent conversation with some artisans that which other artisans had imperfectly, obscurely, and sometimes erroneously explained. . . . With respect to them we had to exercise the function in which Socrates once gloried, the difficult and delicate function of effecting the parturition of souls: *obstetrix animarum*.[75]

[74]D'Alembert, in *Encyclopédie*, p. 97.

[75]D. Diderot, "*Prospectus*," in *Oeuvres complètes*, ed. J. Assézat and M. Tourneux (Paris, 1875–1877), vol. XIII, p. 140. Cf. A. M. Wilson, *Diderot, The Testing Years, 1713–1759* (New York, 1957), esp. pp. 130ff. Wilson's work contains a copious bibliography. For a broad and reasoned discussion of Diderot's literary criticism see P. Casini, "Studi su Diderot," *Rassegna di filosofia* (1958), pp. 5–26, 150–73, 234–54. A. Vartanian, *Diderot and Descartes: a Study of Scientific Naturalism in the Enlightenment* (Princeton, 1953), is wholly lacking in an appraisal of the significance of Diderot's interest in technics and the mechanical arts. Much more useful, from

In the article in the *Encyclopédie* on "Art," which practically constitutes the program of that grandiose work on the mechanical arts on which he was to be engaged for many years, Diderot pointed to the harmful consequences of the traditional distinction between liberal and mechanical arts. This distinction, he contends, has reinforced the prejudice that "to turn one's attention to sensible and material objects" constitutes a derogation of dignity of the human spirit. This prejudice "has filled the cities with proud reasoners and useless contemplatives and the countryside with petty, ignorant, lazy, and disdainful tyrants." But, he continues, this was not how "Bacon, who was one of the first geniuses of England, thought, or Colbert, one of the greatest ministers of France." However, this was still the mode of thought of the French Jesuits who, in the *Avis au public sur la troisième volume de l'Encyclopédie* of 1759, were scandalized precisely over this excessive importance attributed to technical knowledge and to the trades by the followers of the Enlightenment.[76]

To bring to light what for centuries has remained a "fact of practice," what Leibniz had called "the unregistered experience" of the human race—in this Diderot truly felt himself to be a new Socrates.[77] And he, a cutler's son, was truly the heir not only of Bacon, Galileo, and Descartes, but also of those "mechanics" such as Biringuccio, Agricola, Norman, and Palissy, who two centuries before had greatly contributed to the critical undermining of a venerable conception of science which had originated in antique Greece.

---

this point of view, are the essays contained in *L'encyclopédie et le progrès des sciences et des techniques* (Paris, 1952).

[76]F. Venturi, *Le origini dell' Enciclopedia* (Rome, 1946), p. 95.

[77]Diderot, *Oeuvres complètes*, vol. XIII, p. 140, and F. Venturi, *Le origini*, p. 94. For a comprehensive view of this subject see P. Casini, *Diderot "Philosophe"* (Bari, 1962).

Appendix I

The Nature-Art Relationship
and the Machine of the World

The assertion by the major exponents of the new science that there is no substantial difference between the products of art and of nature was radically opposed, as we know, to the Aristotelian definition of art, according to which art completes the work of nature or imitates her in its productions. In Aristotelianism and in Hippocratic medicine (from which the Aristotelian definition very probably derives), nature is presented as an *ideal* which it is the task of art to realize or re-establish, and as a *norm* whose precepts and indications art must follow in order to achieve its aims.[1] The frequent parallels between art and nature in the Aristotelian texts have a precise significance. As Augustin Mansion, among others, has pointed out, they play the role of a "pedagogic procedure" the purpose of which is to facilitate comprehension of what is less familiar (nature) along with the analysis, which is easier for us, of the more familiar procedures of the different arts.[2]

There is certainly no need to recall here the extraordinary

[1]On the relations between art and nature in Aristotle, see A. Mansion, *Introduction à la physique aristotélienne* (Paris, 1945), pp. 94–95, 197, 198–201, 229–234, 256–257. For the Aristotelian definition of art as the imitation of nature, see *Physics*, vol. II, 8, 199a, 15–20; 194a, 21–22; *Meteor*, vol. IV, 3, 381b.

[2]Mansion, *Introduction à la physique*, p. 229. The repertory of all the Aristotelian parallels is found in H. Meyer, *Natur und Kunst bei Aristotles, Ableitung und Bestimmung der Ursachlichkeitsfaktores* (Paderborn, 1919).

success in ancient and medieval thought of the doctrine of
art as *imitatio naturae,* or to recall the innumerable texts in
which art's claim that it could achieve the perfection of nature appears as the fruit of a "Promethean" attitude, the
sign of impiety and extreme boldness.[3] Certainly in the
ambience of this centuries-old tradition, art figures merely
as an attempt to imitate nature and to copy her movements: the mechanical arts appear *adulterinae* precisely
because, as Hugo of Saint Victor asserted, "they borrow
their modes from nature." Nature contains within herself the
principle of an indefinite movement, whereas the products
of art, moved by an external principle, are merely attempts,
doomed to failure, to imitate the spontaneity of natural
movement. This doctrine, explains Bacon, is linked to the
Aristotelian theory of species on the basis of which a
product of nature (tree) is described as having a primary
form, whereas only the attribute of secondary form can be
applied to the product of art (table). Bacon writes in *De
augmentis:*

And I am the more induced to set down the history of arts as
a species of natural history, because an opinion has long been
prevalent, that art is something different from nature, and
things artificial differ from things natural; whence this evil
has arisen: that most writers of natural history think they
have done enough when they have given an account of animals or plants or minerals, omitting all mention of the experiments of mechanical arts. But there is likewise another and
more subtle error which has crept into the human mind:
namely, that of considering art as merely an assistant to nature,
having the power indeed to finish what nature has begun, to
correct her when lapsing into error, or to set her free when in
bondage, but by no means to change, transmute, or funda-
mentally alter nature. And this has bred a premature despair
in human enterprises. Whereas men ought on the contrary to
be surely persuaded of this: that the artificial does not differ
from the natural in forme or essence, but only in the efficient
. . . nor matters it, provided things are put in the way to pro-

[3]P. M. Schuhl, *Machinisme et philosophie* (Paris, 1947), pp. 32–
42, is felicitously instructive on this subject.

duce an effect, whether it be done by human means or otherwise.[4]

Art, therefore, is man added to nature (*ars est homo additus naturae*). The fact that the necessary conditions for the existence of a phenomenon are found necessarily connected or, rather, are placed in relation by the human hand does not create a heterogeneity between natural and artificial phenomena. Hence natural motions are not to be contrasted to artificial motions: solar heat can be compared to that of fire; natural gold present in sand is identical to that artificially produced in the furnaces.[5] Terrestrial physics is identical to celestial physics. The traditional separation of nature and art has produced harmful consequences for the development of knowledge and civilization: "Galen . . . you would have us believe that only Nature can produce a true compound; you snatch at the notion that the heat of the sun and the heat of fire are different things and parade this opinion with the malicious intention of lessening human power wherever you can and of bolstering up ignorance to all eternity through despair of any improvement."[6]

There is a deliberate subversion here of some of the Aristotelian formulations respecting the art-nature relationship. It is asserted that there is no essential distortion between natural and artificial objects. Lightning, which the ancients denied could be imitated, was in fact imitated in the modern epoch. Art is not nature's "ape," and the products of art are not something inferior to natural products. Descartes insists on this point just as forcefully:

There is no difference between the machines built by artisans and the diverse bodies that nature alone composes except the following: the effects of the machine depend solely upon the action of pipes or springs and other instruments which for the

[4]*The Works of Francis Bacon*, ed. R. L. Ellis, J. Spedding, D. D. Heath (London, 1857–1874), I, 496–97.

[5]*Works*, III, 531 (*Temporis partus masculus*); III, 592 (*Cogitata et visa*), I, 497, 624 (*De augmentis*).

[6]*Works*, III, 531 (*Temporis partus masculus*).

reason that they must have some proportion to the hands of those who build them are always so big that their figures and their motions appear visible, whereas the pipes or springs that produce natural effects are generally too small to be perceived by our senses. . . .[7]

The product of art, the machine, serves as a model for the conception and understanding of nature. Art itself is not nature,[8] but art is something similar to a product of art. To understand the functioning of the human body, recourse was still made to the machine:

We see that clocks, artificial fountains, mills, and other machines of this kind, although they have been built by men, do not for this reason lack the power to move by themselves in diverse ways: even respecting that machine which I suppose to have been made by the hands of God, it does not seem possible to me to imagine so many kinds of movement, nor to attribute to it so great an artifice, in such a way as to prevent one from thinking that there can still be many more. . . . Indeed, the nerves can very well be compared to the pipes of machines of those fountains, the muscles and their tendons to the other various contrivances and springs that serve to set them in motion; and their animal spirits to the water that moves them and of which the heart is the fount and the concavities of the brain the tanks. In addition, respiration and other similar natural and ordinary actions of this machine which depend on the course of the spirits, can be compared to the movements of a clock or of a mill which the flow of water can render continuous.[9]

[7]Descartes, *Oeuvres,* ed. Adam and Tannery, vol. IX, p. 321 *(Principia).*

[8]On art as nature, contrast Shakespeare's position in *A Winter's Tale* (IV, iv, 90–92):

> So, over that art
> Which you say adds to nature, is an art
> That nature makes.

On the subject see P. M. Schuhl, "Perdita, la nature et l'art," *Revue de Métaphysique* (1947), and H. Haydn, *The Counter-Renaissance* (New York, 1950), pp. 510ff.

[9]Descartes, *Oeuvres,* vol. IX, pp. 120, 130–31.

The image of the machine and the clock was to enjoy a great success. We find it present also in the works of Kepler, who was preoccupied with the themes of mathematical Pythagorianism:

At one time, steeped in the doctrines of Julius Caesar Scaliger, respecting motor intelligences, I believed that the motor cause of the planets was a soul. . . . The aim that I have set myself here is to affirm that the machine of the universe is not similar to a divine animated being, but similar to a clock (whoever considers the clock to be animated attributes to the work the honor due to the artificer), and in it all the various movements depend upon a simple active material force, in the same manner that all the movements of the clock are due to the simple pendulum.[10]

For Robert Boyle, the universe was a self-moving great machine, "a great piece of clockwork," and all phenomena are to be considered in terms "of the two great and universal principles of bodies: matter and motion."[11]

An extensive discussion respecting the view of animals as machines led to the progressive extension of the mechanical model to human behavior as a whole: "Every Cartesian," wrote the Jesuit Gabriel Daniel, "in order to be consistent, should therefore affirm, with the same seriousness with which he affirms it with respect to beasts, that the other human beings who coexist with him in the world are machines."[12] The line of development that leads from the Cartesian thesis of the animal as a machine to La Mettrie's view of man as a machine has been studied, though not with sufficient breadth, by Busson and Vartanian.[13] It is of

[10]Kepler, *Opera* (1857), vol. I, p. 176; vol. II, p. 84.

[11]Boyle, *Origins of Forms,* in *Works,* ed. Birch, vol. III, p. 14. See also M. Boas, "The Establishment of the Mechanical Philosophy," *Osiris,* vol. X, p. 486; I. B. Cohen, *Franklin and Newton* (Philadelphia, 1956), p. 99.

[12]G. Daniel, *Voyage du monde de Descartes* (Paris, 1703), p. 474. Daniel's work was published in Paris in 1690 and was translated into English (London, 1692) and into Italian (Venice, 1739).

[13]H. Busson, *La religion des classiques, 1660–1683* (Paris, 1948), pp. 121–90; Vartanian, *Diderot and Descartes.*

interest here to recall the text of the article "Méchanicien"
in the great *Encyclopédie:* it expounds the doctrines of
those

Modern doctors who, after the discovery of the circulation of
the blood and the establishment of the philosophy of Descartes,
have shaken off the yoke of authority and have adopted the
methods of geometricians in the investigations which they have
made on the subject of animal economy, considering the latter
a production of movements of different kinds, all subject to the
laws of mechanics. . . . The animal body, and in consequence
the human body, is here considered as a real machine; . . .
medicine assumes a wholly new aspect, a language completely
different from that which had been employed up to then. . . .

The assumption of the model machine, the integral explanation of physical and biological reality in terms of matter and motion, entailed a very profound modification of
the concept of nature. Nature no longer appeared as a context of forms and essences in which "qualities" inhere, but of
phenomena which are quantitatively measurable. All qualities not translatable in mathematical and quantitative terms
were excluded from the world of physics. It was declared
that there were no "hierarchies" in nature and the world no
longer appeared as constructed for man or to the measure
of man. All phenomena, like all the component parts of a
machine, were declared to have the same value. Knowledge
of reality implied an awareness of how the machine of the
world functions, and that machine (at least theoretically)
could be broken down into its single components and put
together again piece by piece. Gassendi writes:

Concerning natural things, we investigate in the same way as
we investigate things of which we ourselves are the authors.
. . . In the things of nature in which this is possible, we make
use of anatomy, chemistry, and aids of all kinds, reducing the
bodies as much as possible, as though decomposing them, to
understand of what elements and according to what criteria
they are composed.[14]

[14]P. Gassendi, *"Syntagma,"* in *Opera omnia* (Lugduni, 1658), vol.
I, pp. 122B–123A.

The world of "reconstructable phenomena, by way of investigation, and of those artificial products which had been created or constructed by the human intellect or by the human hand was declared to be the only world about which any knowledge can be attained. Knowledge of causes and essences was reserved to God, inasmuch as He is the creator and the builder of the world. The later, widespread image of God the "mechanic," constructor of the perfect clock which is the world, was superimposed on the Platonic image of God the geometer. In his commentary on Aristotle's *Mechanical Questions*,[15] Monantheuil wrote that God is a geometer and that Plato had enunciated only a part of the truth: God is first of all a mechanic because the world is a gigantic machine of which He is the builder and artificer.

On the other hand, Sir Thomas Browne remained loyal to the Platonic image of God the geometer; but in defending the Ciceronian position, which held that there was no quarrel between nature and art, and the Aristotelian thesis of art as the perfecting of nature, he also arrived at an image of God as engineer and builder of the world. "Now, nature is not at variance with art, nor art with nature, they being both the service of his providence. Art is the perfection of Nature. Were the world now as it was on the sixth day, there were yet a Chaos. Nature hath made one world, and Art another. In briefe, all things are artificiall, for Nature is the art of God."[16] For Sir Kenelm Digby the world was an immense clock, a wonderous work of the Great Architect, composed of wheels and springs, each one of which can be detached from the mechanism and studied and understood.[17] In Leibniz the image of God as clock-

[15]*Aristoteles Mechanica* (Paris, 1599), *(Praefatio)*.

[16]*The Works of Sir Thomas Browne*, vol. I, ed. Geoffrey Keynes (London, 1964), p. 26.

[17]Sir K. Digby, *Two Treatises, in the One of which, the Nature of Bodies; in the Other, the Nature of Man's Soule is looked Into* (Paris, 1644), pp. 283, 289, 389, 399–400. See also R. T. Petersson, *Sir Kenelm Digby* (London, 1956), p. 185, and in the unpublished

maker was intertwined with that of a God who governs minds and the world "as an engineer manages his machines."[18]

The criterion of knowledge as *making,* or of the identity between cognition and construction, in the view of the exponents of this doctrine, applied to man as much as it did to God. The human intellect, assertedly final and limited, can have access only to those truths which have been structured by men: the truth of physics, of geometry, and of mathematics. Only that which is made, that which is *artificial,* constructed, or reconstructable can be truly known. According to Mersenne:

It is difficult to come upon principles or truths in physics. Inasmuch as the object of physics belongs to the things created by God it should occasion no surprise if we cannot grasp their true causes and the way in which they act and endure. In fact we know the true causes only of those things that we can build with our own hands or intellect, whereas we cannot construct any of those things which God has made.[19]

Hobbes certainly assumed positions that were radically different from those of Mersenne, but on this point he arrived at conclusions that were not dissimilar:

To men is granted knowledge only of things whose generation depends upon their own judgment. Hence the theories concerning quantity, knowledge of which is called geometry, are demonstrable. There is a geometry and it is demonstrable because precisely we ourselves, create the figures. In addition, politics and ethics, namely the knowledge of the just and unjust, of the equitable and unequitable, can be demonstrated

---

texts published by V. Gabrieli, *Sir K. Digby, un inglese italianato nell'età della Controriforma* (Rome, 1957), p. 280. Gabrieli, in contrast to Peterson, exhibits little interest in Digby's philosophical and scientific views.

[18]*Die Philosophischen Schriften von G. W. Leibniz,* ed. G. I. Gerhardt (Berlin, 1875–1890), vol. IV, pp. 479–80; vol. VII, p. 352.

[19]M. Mersenne, *Harmonie universelle* (Paris, 1636), p. 8; see also T. Gregory, *Scetticismo ed empirismo: studio su Gassendi* (Bari, 1961), p. 72. On knowledge as "construction," and on the importance of the "practical arts" in the affirmation of this concept, Gregory's conclusions (pp. 71–77, 160–62) are very illuminating.

a priori: in fact its principles, the conceptions of the just and of the equitable and of their opposites, are known to us because we ourselves create the causes of justice, that is, laws and conventions.[20]

This Hobbesian passage rightly has been compared to a page in Vico in which he proclaims the celebrated principle of *verum factum.* By virtue of experimental physics, declares Vico, in the conclusion of *De antiquissima,* "We hold to be true in nature only that to which, by way of experiment, we succeed in constructing something similar." In an earlier passage in the same work he had asserted: "Consequently, arithmetic and geometry, as well as their child, which is mechanics, are in the faculty of man, inasmuch as in these three fields we demonstrate a truth to the measure that we make it." Hence the comparison between the works of God and the works of man: "Just as God is the artificer of nature, so is man of the things formed by art."[21]

The negation of the Aristotelian doctrine respecting the relations between nature and art, the idea of knowledge as construction, the thesis of the knowability on the part of man, of the products of mind and hand (usually as that world of law, morality, and history that is knowable insofar as it is *made* by man), the assumption of the model *machine* for the explanation and comprehension of the physical world, and the image of God as artificer, engineer, clockmaker: each one of these themes—and they all had a crucial importance—doubtlessly was connected with the gradual penetration of the philosophical and scientific world by a new mode of viewing and appraising that *practice* and those *operations* which for many centuries had been relegated to the margins of culture and deemed unworthy of the attention of scholars and the consideration of academicians.

[20]Thomas Hobbes, *De homine,* X, p. 5, and also *De cive,* XVII, p. 4; *De corpore,* XXV, p. 1.
[21]G. Vico, *Opere,* ed. F. Nicolini (Milan, Naples, 1953), pp. 293, 307.

Appendix II

Truth and Utility in the
Science of Francis Bacon

———◆———

1.

In a treatise on *Intellectual Labor and Manual Labor from Antiquity to the Renaissance*, Rodolfo Mondolfo, with his customary precision and penetration, has brought to light the historical and cultural roots of that radical change in the appraisal of the mechanical arts and of manual labor which took place in Europe between the fifteenth and the sixteenth centuries.[1] The preference shown by Leonardo, Benedetti, and Galileo, and by the Galileans, for mechanics (considered as the method of the sciences because it allows its fruits to be reaped in the practical operation), and the so-called return to Archimedes so frequently stressed by historians of science, were no doubt, as Mondolfo makes very clear, phenomena of an extraordinary importance. In that "preference" and in that "return" lay the manifestation of a cultural revolution which was destined to have unimagined repercussions and to be deeply linked with ongoing changes in economic and social life. Thereby, European culture was led to a definitive break with the thesis of the inferiority of technics vis-à-vis science and of manual labor vis-à-vis intellectual labor which had been vigorously alive in classical and medieval civilization. Mondolfo rightly insists, in this and other essays, on the deficiency of those interpretations which have extended to all

[1]R. Mondolfo, *Alle origini della filosofia della cultura* (Bologna, 1956), pp. 125–49.

classical antiquity the contempt of labor which was manifested by Plato, Aristotle, and the post-Hippocratic physicians. On the one hand, the distinguished scholar points to "the existence of a broad intellectual tendency in the antique world which honors manual labor and the mechanical arts, recognizing their importance for human life and for the development precisely of civilization and intellectuality." However, he explains that in Greece the contempt for manual labor and the mechanical arts originated primarily among the military classes and characterizes "militarist societies and states in their opposition to industrial societies and states."

Nevertheless, Mondolfo is quite aware that what ultimately prevailed in the culture of the antique world was precisely that radical opposition between technics and science which had been militantly opposed by the physicians of the Hippocratic school and those "philosophers of the Greek proletariat," namely the Cynics. In fact, the antithesis was born of the very economic structure of a slave society in which the abundance of "living machines" made superfluous the construction of machines to replace human labor, and in which contempt felt for the slave (or for anyone who engaged in manual activities) is extended to that activity itself.[2] It was precisely this antithesis which was doomed to fall in the centuries of the Renaissance which, according to Dilthey's famous thesis, were characterized "by the union of material labor with the spirit of scientific inquiry." Here was a recognition, Mondolfo claims, "of the importance of practical and experimental production for theoretical knowledge itself." He continues:

It was not only a question of Francis Bacon's aspiration to know nature in order to achieve dominion over her and perfect human life, nor of his conviction that the mechanical arts had

[2]P. M. Schuhl, *Machinisme et philosophie* (Paris, 1947), pp. 13ff.; see on this theme B. Farrington, *Greek Science* (London, 1953), pp. 18–32, 40–41, 104–07, 130–48. The conclusions drawn by S. Samburski, *Il mondo fisico dei Greci* (Milan, 1959), pp. 274ff., are of a much more fragile character.

demonstrated and continued to demonstrate their capacity for progress and continuous perfection, nor even of the idea, expounded later by Locke, that mechanics, held in such great contempt and practiced by illiterate persons, is precisely that human activity that has produced all the arts useful to life. . . . In all these conceptions and other similar ones we always find dominant the idea of a separation and opposition between manual and intellectual work, or at least, with Bacon who wants "knowledge for power," the idea of a relationship which at bottom is a subordination of manual to intellectual work, as an instrument of the application of conquests made in the realm of theory. But in the fullness of its significance the Renaissance view includes the closest and most substantial union between the two forms of labor arising from the consideration that knowledge also is a kind of *making* and involves *making*, whereas, on the other hand, making by itself is a form of cognition and conditions and generates true knowledge.[3]

In confirmation of the thesis expounded here, Mondolfo cites an undoubtedly significant passage from Bruno's *The Expulsion of the Triumphant Beast*.[4]

In my study of the appraisal of the mechanical arts in the sixteenth and seventeenth centuries and the repercussions that this appraisal had in determining the tasks and the very functions of "philosophy," I have also tried to show the close bond that existed between some central theses of Bacon's philosophy and his attitude toward the mechanical arts. On this particular point my researches have led me to conclusions distinctly divergent from those Mondolfo arrived at in the passage just quoted. Since those conclusions have been and still are shared by many historians of philosophy, I shall try to clarify the reason for my dissent here.

2.

I believe that Mondolfo's thesis should be "turned upside down." In other words, I contend that Bacon's philosophy

[3]Mondolfo, *Alle origini della filosofia della cultura*, pp. 147–48.
[4]See pp. 79–80.

was of a very notable cultural significance also because it took a deliberately strong position against the idea of a separation and an opposition between technics and science, manual and intellectual work, and mechanical and liberal arts. Further, I hold that the thesis of "knowledge as a kind of making that involves making" and of "making that is itself a knowledge" doubtlessly was derived from suggestions or hints contained in the books of philosophy and in the treatises on magic and alchemy which appeared during the Renaissance, but which came to its full maturation and rose to a level of keen awareness precisely in the philosophy of the Lord Chancellor.

Baconian historiography has been characterized from its beginning by a polemic which has divided Bacon's interpreters into two great camps: those who view Bacon as a "vulgar utilitarian" and those who feel it is their duty to defend him against this charge by hailing him (despite certain intemperances of language and his zest for polemics) as a "disinterested" appraiser of scientific knowledge. This polemic actually grew out of the fact that the adversaries chose to wage battle on common terrain. The scholars who have critized Bacon's philosophy as one that asserts the superiority of technics over science, of operation over logic, and of the "comforts of life" over philosophy and the scholars who have "defended" him against these criticisms really start out from a very identifiable presupposition, namely, that of an indispensable and ineluctable opposition between technics and science and between "truth" and "utility." This perhaps may explain why scholars in both camps accorded such slight consideration to those arguments which Bacon himself strove to elaborate, and which purposed to assert precisely that such an opposition was both illegitimate and nonexistent.

Scholars, like the chemist and spiritualist philosopher Liebig, who viewed the "search for truth" and the "realization of work" as fields that were absolutely distinct from each other and hierarchically ordered could not but interpret

Bacon's thought as a typical expression of a "vulgar utilitarianism."[5] There have also been interpreters, such as
Fonsegrive, Sortais, Levi, and Anderson, who have dwelt
at length on the passages in which Bacon speaks of truth
as the "supreme good," thereby modifying Liebig's polemical conclusion by shedding light on the "univeralist and
humanistic" character of Bacon's utilitarianism.[6] But even
they, in general, have concluded their arguments by pointing to an "oscillation" in his thought between admiration
for the practical applications of science, on the one hand,
and veneration for a disinterested truth, on the other. This
"oscillation" thesis is expressed with crystalline clarity, for
example, in Levi's work:

Bacon's mind, without any awareness on his part, oscillates
between two different tendencies: turning to the practical application of science, he values the latter for its utility to the
human race; but he tends to assert that knowledge has value
in itself. . . . And the conflict is not removed by the conviction
that *"ipsissimae res sunt veritas et utilitas. . . ."* Humanistic
utilitarianism is the prevailing motive, but it cannot be denied
that, in unconscious conflict with it, a loftier conception of
science and truth is also present in Bacon's thought.[7]

[5]L. von Liebig, *Über F. Bacon von Verulam und die Methode der
Naturforschung* (Munich, 1863), pp. 105, 118.
[6]On the "universalist" character of Baconian utilitarianism, see
G. Fonsegrive, *Francis Bacon* (Paris, 1893), pp. 20ff.; G. Sortais, *La
philosophie moderne depuis Bacon jusqu'à Leibniz* (Paris, 1922),
vol. I, pp. 285ff.; A. Levi, *Il pensiero di F. Bacone considerato in
relazione con le filosofie della Natura del Rinascimento e col razion-
alismo cartesiano* (Turin, 1925), pp. 168–69. F. Anderson, *The
Philosophy of Francis Bacon* (Chicago, 1948), makes a "rationalist"
of Bacon and rejects the traditional interpretations, including that of
utilitarianism. B. Farrington's book, *F. Bacon, Philosopher of Industrial Science* (New York, 1949), is the most important attempt to
overcome the traditional alternative to which we have referred in the
text. A. R. Hall, *The Scientific Revolution, 1500–1800* (London,
1954), pp. 164ff., while excessively stressing the opposition between
his theses and Farrington's, rightly notes that in Bacon's thought the
validity of the method is that which guarantees the production of
works. J. G. Crowther, *Francis Bacon, the First Statesman of Science*
(London, 1960), sees in Bacon the expression of a new type of intellectual interested in the problems of the utilization and of the organization of science, of its "integration" into the life of society.
[7]Levi, *Il pensiero di F. Bacone*, p. 169.

The presupposition (and the "prejudice") at the base of a judgment of this type is strikingly evident: namely, the assertion that knowledge as a "value for itself" constitutes something that is "loftier" than any attempt to conjoin "truth" and "utility."

In the course of these pages I propose: (1) to indicate the radical deficiencies of those interpretations (quite numerous and full of qualifications) where Bacon has been seen as a typical representative of utilitarianism; and (2) to clarify the significance that should be attributed to the controversial assertion Bacon makes in paragraph 124 of the *Novum organum* that has most often been interpreted with scant exactness: *"ipissimae res sunt veritas et utilitas."*

3.

What Bacon forcefully rejected and what made traditional knowledge appear to him like a "barren desert" was, above all else, the fact that from the pre-Socratics to Telesio, truth had appeared as something separate from and opposed to utility, introducing a cleavage between knowledge and operation, between logical discourse and experimental techniques. Bacon asserted instead the identity of knowledge and power, theory and practice, truth and utility, and considered opposition between these terms as exceedingly harmful. One of the most interesting, indeed we might say "topical," aspects of Bacon's philosophy is the attempt he made to show how the opposition came about and was steadily reinforced in the history of mankind. In Bacon's view it is not "philosophy" which forces a crisis on this opposition; rather, the crisis is engendered by that series of grandiose changes which have taken place in the course of time and modified human civilization.

We must refer in particular to the character and situation of previous civilizations, according to Bacon, if we are to understand the origins of that opposition and the causes underlying its consolidation through the centuries. The project of a literary history (today we would call it a "history of ideas") expounded in the *Advancement of Learning* (1605) is indicative of Bacon's standpoint. The task of literary history is the description of the state and condition of human culture in various epochs. It is not a question of writing a *special* history (of, say, jurisprudence, rhetoric, or mathematics) or a "memorial" history, but a history of the origins and development of all knowledge, of the birth and flowering of scientific schools, of their struggles, their decadence, and their decline into oblivion. Such a history would attempt to determine the "causes and occasions" of this development and of this decline. In subsequent years, while preparing the translation and amplification of the *Advancement,* Bacon was to indicate even more explicitly what he understood by the word "cause"; the different "natures" of regions and peoples, what would have to be determined are the characteristics of the latter that are favorable or unfavorable to the rise of particular sciences, and the accidental causes that foster or retard the progress of culture. The relations between culture and religious life and between culture and laws would also have to be clarified; and the efficacy of individual men in the promotion of sciences would have to be indicated, etc. Therefore a history conceived along such lines must reflect, as it traverses the various epochs of history, all those events that have a bearing on cultural life. It is not to be written for the purpose of curiosity or personal satisfaction, but it should have a "more serious and grave purpose"—that of teaching men to make conscious use of their knowledge."[8]

Bacon did not fail to apply these precepts in the course of that vast "history of philosophy" which he scattered in bits and pieces through his various works. He saw a close relation between the failure to develop investigations of a physical type—the "contemplative" character of Greek, Roman, and medieval philosophy—and the historical con-

---

[8]Bacon, *Works,* ed. Ellis, *et al.,* III, 330 (*Advancement of Learning*); I, 503–04 (*De augmentis*). See also Flugel, "Bacon's *Historia Literarum,*" *Anglia,* XII (1899).

ditions that were peculiar to these civilizations. Greek philosophy "took its rise in an age that bordered on fables, was poor in historical knowledge, and was little informed or enlightened by travel and knowledge of the earth." The great voyages of Pythagoras, Democritus, and Plato "were rather suburban excursions than distant journeys," hence the "limitedness" of the Greek mind and the "disputatious" character of this civilization. In Roman times "the size of the Empire claimed the exertions of many," and the best minds turned to problems of politics instead of those of natural philosophy. In the Middle Ages those who applied their intellect to theology were the recipients of "the most handsome rewards and generous aids." This once more caused men to turn away from the world of nature, and philosophers then "rich in idleness and sharp of wit" lived cloistered lives between the cells of convents, exercising their extremely sharp wits on Aristotle's texts.[9]

An integral part of Bacon's *Instauratio magna* was criticism directed against the philosophical tradition. This work did not have a "speculative" purpose, and through the *Instauratio* Bacon intended to "entreat men to believe that there is not an opinion to be held, but a work to be done, and to be well assured that I am labouring to lay the foundation, not of any sect or doctrine, but of human utility and power." In order to realize this labor it is not enough to "reform logic"; before all else men must be made aware of the identity between progress in theory and prog-

[9]Bacon, *Works*, ed. Ellis *et al.*, III, 595–97, 601 (*Cogitata et visa*); III, 563–65, 570 (*Redargutio philosophiarum*); and *Novum organum*, I, 71–72, 79–80 for the judgment on Greek philosophy. For that on scholasticism see III, 187 (*Cogitationes de scientia humana*); III, 285–87 (*Advancement of Learning*); I, 453–55 (*De augmentis*); *Novum organum*, I, 89, 121. On the significance of "history" in Bacon's thought see P. Rossi, *F. Bacone* (Bari, 1957), pp. 132–48, 191–208, and E. De Mas "Bacone e Vico," *Filosofia* (1959), pp. 505–59. But there are still some scholars who speak of Bacon as the "initiator of the experimental method" who was lacking "a sense of the historicity of knowledge," for example R. Franchini, *Il progresso, storia di un'idea* (Milan, 1960), pp. 26, 29.

ress in practice, between the strengthening of cognitive instruments and the strengthening of man's operative capacities.

To assert that for Bacon the *capacity* to produce "works is the guarantee of the truth of the method" is perfectly legitimate only on the condition that, at the same time, it is realized that, according to the Lord Chancellor, "only a true method is able to produce real works."[10] It is opportune at this point to recall several Baconian texts.

Bacon had already posited the sovereignty of man in knowledge in the "conference of pleasure" of 1592, entitled *The Praise of Knowledge*. Indeed, precisely when he affirmed that the aim of knowledge was to serve life, he identified man with "that which man knows."[11] In *De sapientia verterum (The Wisdom of the Ancients)*, published in 1609, where he interprets the myth of the Sphinx, Bacon found a way to reaffirm this human dependence upon scientific knowledge. The riddles posed by the Sphinx are of two kinds: those respecting the nature of things and those respecting the nature of man. Only he who succeeds in knowing nature will be able to dominate her, and only by knowing human nature will it be possible to acquire dominion over the natural world.[12]

Bacon expressed the thesis of the identity between truth and utility in a series of different formulations. It is opportune to present the following brief analytic description of them here because very often these different formulations have been isolated from their contexts. Bacon's concern in

[10]This has been clearly perceived by G. Preti, "Dewey e la filosofia della scienza," *Rivista critica di storia della filosofia*, IV (1951), pp. 290–91: "In reality Bacon has already pointed out how practicality without truth is indeed merely a mediocre practicality." In this article, while referring to Dewey's "Baconianism," Preti clarifies the significance of the truth-utility relation in contemporary pragmatism and sees in Bacon and in Hume the first champions of this type of relation.
[11]J. Spedding, *The Letters and Life of Francis Bacon, including All His Occasional Works* 7 vols. (London, 1861–1872), I, 123–25.
[12]*Works*, ed. Ellis *et al.*, VI, 679.

Partis instaurationis secundae delineatio et argumentum, in *Cogitata et visa,* and later in the *Novum organum,* was to reply to an easily foreseeable objection, one which could easily be raised from the viewpoint of traditional philosophy: is not the contemplation of truth worthier and loftier than any practical invention, no matter how important and useful the latter may be? Cannot the continuous insistence on work, on practical results, and on the "arts" sound justly excessive, displeasing, and unwelcome to the person who dedicates his every love and veneration to meditation? Does not this dawdling with and "dwelling with experience and matter" remove the mind from the serenity and tranquility that are proper to learning?[13]

It is strange to note that those who have talked about "Baconian utilitarianism" have often based their arguments on the foundations of the very questions to which Bacon earnestly endeavored to give a reply. Disputable as it may be, Bacon's reply was explicit and exact with respect to the aforementioned questions. Indeed, in the last analysis it aimed to preclude even the possibility that his position could be mistaken as one that smacked of utilitarianism. Bacon's reply is outlined in two distinct modes: (1) In *Partis instaurationis secundae delineatio* Bacon affirms that he, who in the name of the contemplative life protests against the excessive insistence on work, goes against his own desires, because the purity of the contemplation as well as invention and construction of works are based almost on virtually the same things and are enjoyed together ("*cum puritas contemplationum atque substructio et inventio operum prorsus eisoem rebus nitartur et simul perfruantur*");[14] (2) His reply is more explicit and decisive in *Cogitata et visa* and in the *Novum organum.* In the former work Bacon affirms that man's mastery resides only in science, and that man possesses power to the extent that he possesses knowledge. The defender of the rights of con-

---

[13]*Ibid.,* III, 459, 612; *Novum organum,* I, 124.
[14]*Works,* ed. Ellis *et al.,* III, 540.

templation goes counter to his own desires because practical results are not only beneficial to life but are also pledges of truth *("Opera non tantum vitae beneficia, sed et veritatis pignora sunt")*. Just as in religion each is asked to show his faith in works, so in natural philosophy it is asked that learning be demonstrated by practical results.

Results, in fact, are able to demonstrate truth more than "argumentation" or "immediate experience." This assertion rests on the conviction that a single and identical norm governs the progress of the condition and the mind of man *("quare unam eademque ratione et conditionis humanae et mentis dotandae esse")*.[15] In paragraph 124 of the first book of the *Novum organum*, instead of highlighting the contradiction inherent in the questions of the espousal of contemplation, Bacon explicitly accepts his very conclusions. The demands that are expressed through those questions, he states, are perfectly legitimate. But these questions do not constitute a valid objection, because all that is suggested respecting the value of contemplation or of "theory" is wholly realized precisely in the ambit of the reform of knowledge. The image of the world which the reform proposes to yield is not in fact relative to individual reason, but to what is "veracious" and "in conformity with reality." The "fantastic" philosophies that have "aped" nature are but the expression of the confused idols of the human mind, that is, arbitrary abstractions *("abstractiones ad placitum")*. Rather, the real question is to arrive at the comprehension of the true stamp imposed by the Creator on creatures *("vera signacula Creatoris super creaturas")*. In this respect *things themselves*, as such, are at one and the same time truth and utility, and works themselves must be esteemed more as pledges of truth than that they be pursued because of the comforts of life they afford *("atque ipsissimae res sunt, in hoc genere, veritas et utilitas: atque opera ipsa pluris facienda sunt, quatenus sunt veritatis pignora, quam propter vitae commoda")*.

[15]*Ibid.*, III, 612.

4.

"Is not the contemplation of truth worthier and loftier than any practical invention no matter how important and useful it may be?" Bacon, at different times, gave different replies to this same question. Before clarifying the relationship that intervenes between these replies and the development of Bacon's thought, we must pause to analyze the significance of the passage from the *Novum organum* which was quoted at the end of the preceding paragraph. There has been no lack of conflicting interpretations concerning this passage, and many interpreters have translated *"ipsissimae res sunt veritas et utilitas"* as if *truth* and *utility* are the very same thing. Upon closer scrutiny the accuracy of that translation, which has gained wide currency, appears difficult to sustain. Spedding himself, who was its most authoritative defender, felt compelled to give up justifying this use of the term *ipsissimae* on Bacon's part. "I do not think that the use of *ipsissimae* can be justified if the meaning be (as I think it must) that the truth and utility are (in this kind) the very same things."[16] Those who have followed Spedding's translation (to cite some: Levi, Banfi, Canfora, Saloni, and Anderson)[17] have not even expressed the doubts which the greatest authority on Bacon felt duty bound to mention, but neither have they come up with any justification of their own translation.

In my opinion the aforementioned translation is untenable for two reasons: (1) Bacon knew Latin well enough to use *idem* correctly in place of *ipse*—for example, *"ista duo pronuntiata activum et contemplativum, res eadem sunt."* Indeed, we could cite an extraordinary number of such examples here; (2) The phrase *ipsissimae res*, or the

[16]*Ibid.,* I, 218, note 1.
[17]See Levi, *Il Pensiero di F. Bacone,* p. 169, and the translations of the *Novum organum* by A. Banfi (Milan, 1943), p. 109; by Canfora (Bari, 1938), p. 163; by A. Saloni (Florence, 1942), p. 139; and by Anderson, *The Philosophy of Francis Bacon,* p. 188.

term *ipsissimus,* which were widely used in scholastic terminology, recur in other passages of the *Novum organum* with a precise, technical meaning. In my opinion the deficiency of the above-mentioned interpretations or translations derives from the fact that their authors did not bear in mind these other uses of the term. Ignoring Spedding's suggestion, they have understood "*ipsissimae res sunt veritas et utilitas*" to mean "truth and utility are in this kind the very things we seek for" (Ellis), or "the chief things of all are, in this kind, truth and usefulness" (Kitchin), or finally "the very things themselves (this is the facts of nature) are, in this kind of inquiry, both truth and utility" (Fowler).[18] Even the author of the last translation, who has written one of the best commentaries on the *Novum organum,* and whose rendering unquestionably comes closest to accuracy, has not taken into consideration the other passages in Bacon's work, to which we shall now refer.

In paragraph 137 of the second book of the *Novum organum,* Bacon defines form as "*ipsissima res,*" affirming that the thing only differs from its object as the apparent from the actual object, or the exterior from the interior, of that which is considered with relation to man from that which is considered with relation to the universe ("*cum enim forma rei sit ipsissima res; neque differat res a forma aliter quam differunt apparens et existens, aut exterius at interius, aut in ordine ad hominem aut in ordine ad universum*").

In paragraph 20 of the second book Bacon used the term *ipsissimus* and spoke of "*ipsissimus calor sive quid ipsum caloris.*" For Bacon, as is well known, there is a radical difference between common experience and scientific experience. Moreover, he contended that all natural phenomena are reducible to a finite number of simple elements. The objective nature of heat is determinable through an investigation which, by going beyond sensible

<hr/>

[18]See Bacon's *Novum organum,* ed. T. Fowler (Oxford, 1889), p. 329, which also contains the other translations cited in the text.

appearances, aims to pin-point the presence of particular conditions of a geometro-mechanical kind. Such conditions constitute heat in its objective state, that is to say, considered not *"ex analogia hominis,"* in relation to man, but *"ex analogia universi,"* in relation to the universe. According to Bacon's view, heat is a species of the genus "motion." It is not to be thought that heat generates motion or is generated by it; rather, the very essence of heat, or the substantial self of heat, is motion and nothing else (*"ipsissimus calor sive quid ipsum caloris motus et nihil aliud est"*).

Given the fact that the relation between heat and motion is that of species to genus, some differences are enumerable which limit the motion and constitute it in the form of heat. In question here is an expansive, rapid motion, tending upwards, which does not belong to the entire given body but to its parts. The definition of heat obtained through the first vintage (*"vindemiatio prima"*) is at once speculative and operative; if it is possible to produce in a given natural body a motion exhibiting the characteristics indicated in the definition (*"espansivus, cohibitus, nitens per partes minores,"* etc), heat will infallibly be generated (*"proculdubio generabis calidum"*). A close examination of these two passages in the *Novum organum* leads one to assert: (1) that the expression *ipsissimae res* and the term *ipsissimus* were used by Bacon in reference to the "objective reality of things," or to "things in their reality," or simply to "essence" (in the particular meaning that Bacon gives to this term), or to "form" which has been defined as *"ipsissima res"*; (2) that the use of these terms appears directly linked to a consideration of reality *"ex analogia universi"* and not *"ex analogia hominis"*; (3) that the use of these terms also appears linked to the central theme of Bacon's philosophy, namely, that of an *"expurgatio intellectus"* which is to transform the human mind—compared to an "enchanted mirror"—into a clear mirror capable of reflecting the structures of natural reality.

In Bacon's view the human mind "left to itself" (that is,

without any technique of verification and any method of approach to reality) is "a thing unequal, and quite unfit to contend with the obscurity of things."[19] The products of the "free" mind are but "idols," namely ineffectual and arbitrary opinions (*placita quaedam inania*"), whereas the ideas of the divine mind "are the true signatures and marks set upon the works of creation as they are found in nature" ("*Verae signaturae atque impressionae factae in creaturis prout inveniuntur*").[20] Man must liberate himself from "idols" if he is to arrive at the reality of things, these divine "marks" imprinted by God. In paragraph 124 of the *Novum organum* (a few lines above the passage with which we are here concerned) Bacon explicitly returned to this thesis, distinguishing once more between idols and divine ideas. From this point of view the meaning of his statements can be clarified and summed up as follows: *things as they really are, considered not from the viewpoint of appearance but from that of existence, not in relation to man but in relation to the universe, offer conjointly truth and utility.* In other words, only where the human mind forsakes its state of arbitrary freedom (i.e., the state of being "left to itself") and learns to make use of specific techniques of inquiry, will it be able to arrive at the knowledge of natural facts in their objective form. Furthermore, it is only from this point of view (which, moreover, is that of science and method, in contrast to that of the various "fantastic" philosophies) that theoretical truths and operative rules are united and identical.

5.

The coincidence of knowledge and power, of truth and utility, and the convertibility of theory into operations, presupposes, therefore, the adoption on the part of the intellect of precise technical rules and logical instruments

[19]*Novum organum*, I, 21.
[20]*Novum organum*, I, 23.

capable of amplifying its powers and limits, as well as verifying and ensuring its progress. In other words, only the adoption of the "new method" guarantees this coincidence which is nowhere present or in no way realizable where the mind is without instruments or contends that it can work without them. With the human mind "left to itself" there is only a place for the fantastic constructions of the traditional philosophies of nature which are doomed to sterility, or for the reduction of philosophy to a rhetorical exercise which renders it suitable exclusively for serving the needs of civil life or of making human conversation more pleasing.

From Bacon's point of view, the question as to whether scientific truth depends on the procedures employed to affirm them, or on their fruitfulness in practice, is a meaningless dilemma: a scientific truth is always fruitful and this fruitfulness depends precisely and exclusively on its characteristic of full truth. The twin human intentions Bacon stated, namely knowledge and power, coincide in a single intention, and ignorance of causes produces the failure of works: that which is considered a cause in the theoretical sphere is considered a rule in the operational sphere. (*"Quod in contemplatione instar causae est, id in operatione instar regulae est."*)[21] This implies that the designation *cause* cannot be legitimately applied to a cause which cannot at the same time also be considered a *rule,* and vice versa. It is a question of obtaining causes from experiments and new experiments from these causes. This, however, involves not two processes but only one, because theoretical research and practical application are but the "same experience which is constituted in two different ways." Placed in front of a certain effect or of a certain nature, "contemplation" proceeds to the investigation of the cause, whereas an "operation," starting with precisely the same cause and using it as a *means,* tries to achieve par-

[21]*Works,* ed. Ellis *et al.,* I, 144 (*Distributio operis*); see also III, 553–54 (*Partis inst. secundae delineatio*), and *Novum organum,* I, 3.

ticular effects and to have a given body achieve a certain
nature. Every experiment, turned upside down, is a practical operation.[22] In Baconian terminology a "perfect operation in this way corresponds to a "true precept"; theoretical
investigation and practical application are the same, and
what is most useful in practice is most correct in theory.
*("Ista autem duo pronuntiota, activum et contemplativum,
res eadem sunt; et quod in operando utilissimum, id in
sciendo verissimum.")*[23]

6.

Bacon's paramount interest was to prevent the consideration of the progress of theoretical constructions and the
progress of the human condition as "separate" or even
"opposed" processes, as philosophy had done from the time
of Socrates and Plato. Hence it was necessary not only to
affirm the view of the convergence of truth and utility, but
also to avoid placing truth in a "relation of dependency"
in respect to utility. In Bacon's view, practicality without
truth is arbitrary and casual, thus incapable of progress
and development. The hunt for immediate, practical results
is typical of the procedures of magic and alchemy: this
frenzy to achieve practical results is directly related to the
deficient and incomplete character of the "theories" that
guided the operations of magicians and alchemists. They
had an individual subjective character, which was neither

[22]Viano, *Esperienza e natura nella filosofia di F. Bacone*, vol. III,
p. 301: "At bottom, theoretical inquiry and practical application are
but two modes of configuration of the same experiment, and every
experiment, turned upside down, is a practical application." Viano
also concludes, however, by adhering to the famous "utilitarian"
thesis and speaks of the "merely instrumental character of cognition
with respect to operation" (p. 296). From this point of view, we can
understand how he can arrive at conclusions which in my opinion
are difficult to accept. For Viano, Bacon would be the philosopher
who "did not ask himself what operation means and what a place
this operation should have in the life of a man or of a society" (p.
312).

[23]*Novum organum*, II, 4.

communicable nor codifiable. Actually, that "theoretical apparatus" was not an apparatus proper to the task because it was lacking in terminological rigor, communicability, and intersubjectivity. On the contrary, in his polemic against magico-alchemist procedures, Bacon set forth the requirement of rigorous and codifiable methods; he affirmed that "works must be esteemed more as pledges of truth than for the comforts of life they afford." (*Opera ipsa pluris facienda sunt, quatenus sunt veritatis pignora, quam propter vitae commoda.*)[24] Evidently we are not dealing here with a casual coincidence: there is a clear and distinct relation between this statement and that demand. In the name of the rights of "theory," Bacon took a position against the empiricists "who gather the wheat when it is still green," or he referred to the myth of Atalanta, who lost the contest for having chased after the golden apples, or he affirmed the necessity of giving precedence to *"experimenta lucifera"* over *"experimenta fructifera"*—the latter aiming at immediate results whereas the former are conducted for the purpose of establishing axioms and determining a technique of verifying these same axioms.[25] This preoccupation with the theoretical apparatus of scientific research appears particularly evident in *Partis instaurationis secundae delineatio* (1607) in which "the technique of verifying the axioms seems to have a preponderant part with respect to their efficacy."[26] I think the word "seems" is very important in this proposition (also in the case of the *Delineatio*), because it is not possible to see an admission, on Bacon's part, of a separation between the two attitudes—the contemplative and the operative—"both being considered legitimate." Anderson, who has energetically upheld this thesis, has written that the *Delineatio*, in contrast to the other works, "separates the contemplative function" of knowledge from

[24]*Works*, ed. Ellis *et al.*, III, 612 (*Cogitata et visa*); *Novum organum*, II, 4.
[25]*Works*, ed. Ellis *et al.*, I, 141; III, 498; VI, 668; *Novum organum*, I, 70, 99, 117, 121.
[26]Viano, *Esperienza e natura*, p. 301.

the "operative." Unfortunately, Anderson does not go beyond an analysis of the text, which is insufficiently pursued
in depth.[27]

The work of reason, wrote Bacon in the *Delineatio*, is of
a twofold character and can have a twofold end and use.
Man's finality can be that of knowing or contemplating,
or that of acting or operating, and he investigates either
the cognition of causes or the abundance of effects. The
aim of knowledge is to know the cause of a particular
effect, and the aim of power is to introduce a certain
nature into a particular "material base." Anderson founded
his argument on this distinction and interrupted his expo-
sition of the text at this point. Actually Bacon introduced
the distinction in a provisional way, for immediately thereafter he adds:

These two proposals, to whomever inspects them more attentively and truly examines them, end up as one, because that
which in contemplation is as the cause is, in operation, as the
rule. (*Hae intentiones, acutius inspicienti et vere aestimanti
in iden coincidunt. Nam quod in contemplatione instar causae
est, in operatione est instar medii*).[28]

Moreover, Bacon at this point furnished a real justification for the distinction which he introduced, but Anderson
does not take it into consideration. What is at stake here
is an interesting passage which can be useful for clarifying
Bacon's attitude toward this problem and which Bacon was
to take up again (in a different sense) in the *Novum
organum*. There would be no reason for the distinction
between knowing and operating, wrote Bacon, if all the
means necessary for works were at man's disposal. Given
man's multiple necessities and the fact of human weakness,
the capacity to operate is confined within limits that are
narrower than those granted to knowledge. From this it

[27]Anderson, *The Philosophy of Francis Bacon*, p. 90.
[28]*Works*, ed. Ellis *et al.*, III, p. 554 (*Partis inst. secundae delineatio*).

follows that in practical activity very often the result is to demand "a certain ability in the choice of that which is immediately available" rather than a "free and universal" knowledge of what can be accomplished. For this reason, concluded Bacon, it is opportune for the purposes of the treatment of the subject to introduce the distinction between knowledge and operation, and between the investigation of causes and the utilization of effects. Hence the cleavage between the two terms, according to Bacon, is due to the fact that human operations are actually entrusted to an immediate "prudence," as it were, and to a series of perceptions of an empirical and "artisan" character neither sustained nor guided by a method and lacking any generality or universality. Bacon intended to explode these narrow limits that determine human operation; for to give men the possibility of "operating freely" is tantamount to broadening their knowledge of causes and to substitute "fantastic" theories by "true" theories.

In the *Novum organum,* apart from the *Delineatio,* it seems to some interpreters that Bacon reversed his position. Here, he asserts that given the

pernicious and inveterate habit of dwelling upon abstractions, it is by far the safest method to commence and build up the sciences from those foundations which bear a relation to the practical division and to let them mark out and limit the theoretical. *(Propter perniciosam et inveteratem consuetudinem versandi in abstractis, tutius omino est ordiri et excitare scientias ab iis fundamentis quae in ordine sunt ad partem activam, ut illa ipsa partem contemplativam signet et determinet.)*[29]

In order to achieve this aim, Bacon makes careful use of the description of an operation ("to generate or impose any nature upon a given body") in order to show as clearly as possible what precepts and what procedures are to be followed, and to determine, in consequence, the "true axiom" or the theoretical formulation to be employed in

[29]*Novum organum,* II, 4.

every operation directed at effecting the transformation of
a given body.

Hence it seems that there is no justification for the frequently repeated assertion that the *Delineatio* presents a
separation of theory and practice which is then negated
in the *Novum organum.* Bacon's position in the *Delineatio*
differs from that presented in the *Novum organum* only in
this sense: in the former Bacon contended that it is more
opportune to depend on an analysis of axioms or general
propositions in order to modify the relation between theory
and practice (or between truth and utility) instituted by
the traditional philosophers, whereas in the latter Bacon
maintained that methodologically it would be far safer to
initiate the reform of knowledge from "practice" (or from
operations) rather than to start from theory. In the first
case he based himself on the *greater* freedom of theoretical
constructions vis-à-vis the immediacy that characterizes
"casual" operations; in the second case he leaned on the
description of "organized" operations to expose the arbitrary character of traditional "theories."

It is no accident that from *Temporis partus masculus*
to *Redargutio philosophiarum,* and from the *Cogitata et
visa* to the *Novum organum,* Bacon, for almost twenty
years, insistently dwelt on a twofold criticism directed as
much against the "deficiency" of the work of the empiricists
as against the abstractness and arbitrariness of the theories
of the rationalists. It was a polemic conducted on two
fronts, so to speak:

The study of nature with a view to works is engaged in by the
mechanic, the mathematician, the physician, the alchemist, and
the magician—but all (as things now are) with slight endeavor
and scanty success. . . . The works already known are due to
chance and experiment rather than to science. . . .
    Anticipations are a ground sufficiently firm for consent, for
even if men went mad all after the same fashion, they might
agree one with another well enough. . . . The rational school
of philosophers snatches from experience a variety of common
instances, neither duly ascertained nor diligently examined

and weighed, and leaves all the rest to meditation and agitation of wit. . . .[30]

Even where Bacon introduces a distinction between the speculative part and the operative part of natural philosophy, or, as in *De augmentis*[31] (which is his work most linked to tradition and to classification already culturally codified, between an "ascending scale" (which rises from experiences to general propositions), and a "descending scale" (which descends from general propositions to new inventions), he does not deny or contradict his thesis of the identity of knowledge and power, truth and utility, and cause and rule. The separation that is introduced between the terms in each pair is always presented as provisional and preparatory; it has an exact meaning within the context of an attempt to reform the actual conditions of science. The distinction loses some meaning within the framework of a science that has overcome a situation of operational uncertainty and theoretical arbitrariness, which, according to Bacon, characterized the whole of knowledge in his time. This uncertainty and arbitrariness are at one and the same time the cause and the effect of the cleavage between truth and utility. If this situation "which seems to have no way out" is to be relieved, man must adopt a new attitude toward natural reality and successfully re-establish with nature "a contact" that has been lost, and he must learn to view the world not *"ex analogia hominis"*—in relation to man, but *"ex analogia universi"*—in relation to the world. In view of these aims, it was necessary to arrive at a new definition of man (no longer considered as a rational animal, but as a "servant and interpreter of nature"), and to formulate a new scientific method—establish a natural history based on the new philosophy, and reorganize the entire corpus of knowledge.

When Bacon accused Aristotle of having entertained the

[30]*Ibid.*, I, 5, 8, 27, 62.
[31]*Works,* ed. Ellis *et al.,* I, 547.

pretention "to produce" the world by way of a series of
verbal distinctions, or protested against "cobwebs" constructed with great mental acuity by the Scholastics, his
aim was to strike at a logic which from his point of view
was an obstacle to every effective procedure for the investigation of nature.

Bacon grants that such logic doubtlessly can teach men
how to extract themselves from difficulties in disputes, but
it cannot help them either to establish true axioms or, in
consequence, to effect fruitful operations. It involves a
logic "superimposed on things" which substitutes conceptual abstraction for what is known as "matter," "void,"
"dense," and "rare." But for Bacon this sterility (and this
can never be overly emphasized) does not depend on the
fact that its logic is composed of abstractions but on the
fact that such abstractions: (1) are "beautiful and probable
opinions rather than certain and demonstrated cognitions";
(2) are obtained through the use of an erroneous and hasty
method; and (3) consequently they compel only assent,
instead of also compelling nature.[32] Only the hastiness of
certain interpretations can explain the fact that some
scholars have seen in Bacon a kind of negator of the rights
of "knowledge" or "logic." "The dry light of logic," wrote
the Lord Chancellor, "offends the moist and soft minds of
many persons."[33] To be sure, he did not place himself
among the latter, and the "interpretations of nature" with
which he intended to replace the "anticipations" of traditional logic are not at all less "abstract than the anticipa-

[32]*Ibid.*, I, 154 (*Praefatio*); *Novum organum*, I, 18, 29.

[33]*Works*, ed. Ellis *et al.*, I, 616: "Pars ista humanae philosophiae
quae ad logicam spectat, ingeniorum plurimorum gustui ad palato
minus gratat, est, et nihil aliud videtur quam spinosae subtilitatis
laqueus et tendicula. . . . Eodem modo (ut plurimum) illae scientiae
placent quae habent infusionem nonnullam carnium magis esculen-
tam, quales sunt historia civilis, mores, prudentia politica, circa quas
hominum cupiditates, laudes, fortunae vertuntur et occupatae sunt.
Ad istud lumen siccum plurimorum mollia et madida ingenia offen-
dit et torret. Caeterum unamquamque rem propria si placet dignitate
metiri, rationales scientiae reliqurum omnio claves sunt."

tions." On the contrary, while anticipations "straightway touch the understanding and free the imagination" interpretations "cannot suddenly strike the understanding; and therefore they must needs, in respect of the opinions of the time, seem harsh and out of tune, much as the mysteries of faith do."[34]

Bacon is opposed to two phenomena which occur in traditional logic: (a) the system of logical relations, or the rules of discourse, that is declared to be self-sufficient and furnished with intrinisic finalities; and (2) the necessity of operations capable of applying such rules and significations to natural reality is ignored. From these two points, according to Bacon, can be derived that character which is common to all thought that has been handed down by tradition: the requisites of natural discourse have been assumed as the measure of natural reality. For Bacon, rather, it is precisely the "operations" which constitute the discourse to which it should refer and thus strip logic of its character of discourse that had been isolated and completely separated from the operations in which it functions: *"prolatio verborum contemplativa aut operativa re non differunt. Cum enim hoc dicis: lumen non est ex forma caloris; idem est si dicis: in calore producendo non necesse est ut etiam lumen producas."*[35]

This is not the opportune place to examine the origins and the limits of the reform of logic attempted by Bacon. All that we shall point out here is that an attitude of this kind presupposed an appraisal of the procedures, methods, and instruments employed in the labor of artisans and technicians which deliberately placed itself in antithetical opposition to those operative in the traditional culture. For Bacon the awareness of the identity between progress in theories and progress in the human condition was certainly an indispensable element in the very formation of a project for the restoration and reform of learning, but it is equally

[34]*Novum organum*, I, 28.
[35]*Works*, ed. Ellis *et. al.*, III, 794 (*Aphorismi et consilia*).

true that the identity of knowledge and power, truth and
utility presented itself to him more as an end to be realized
through reform rather than as an achievable goal. It was
not by chance that he saw the guarantee of the absolute
operativeness of scientific knowledge and of the full coincidence between knowing and operating precisely in the
doctrine of forms, which is the culmination of the method
and represents the ultimate goal of all natural philosophy.
The path of truth and power is the same, wrote Bacon, in
Aphorisma et consiliae. Briefly, it is the forms of things
that are to be found; from the knowledge of forms derives
"*contemplatio vera*" and "*operatio libera*" ("*eadem est veritatis et potestatis via et perfectio; haec ipsa, ut formae
rerum inveniantur: ex quarum notitia sequitur contemplatio
vera et operatio libera*").[36] This passage also constitutes a
confirmation of the previous interpretation that we have
suggested of paragraph 124 of the first book of the *Novum
organum.*

Mario Manlio Rossi has perceptively observed that the
difference between Bacon's utilitarianism and that of modern science consists in the fact that modern science does
not tell us, as does Bacon, that science *must serve,* but
that it *really serves.* "Modern utilitarianism," continues
Rossi, "does not concede (something which Bacon conceded
and therefore fought) that science can ever be a pure theoretical construction, in no way influenced by human aims
and by human needs."[37] I do not share this view either—
as regards the opportuneness of using the term "utilitarianism" in this case, or as regards his appraisal of Bacon as
a "philosopher of technics" on the basis of this distinction.
In the historical situation in which Bacon operated, his
philosophical attitude necessarily had to take the form of
an attempt to establish a hierarchy of values between the
"verbose" learning that he assertedly had put behind him
and the new learning that he felt it his duty to inaugurate.

[36]*Ibid.*, III, 794.
[37]M. M. Rossi, *Saggio su F. Bacone* (Naples, 1935), p. 156.

This is why, in his work, the thesis of the identification of knowledge and power, and truth and utility, is never presented as a simple confirmation of fact, but assumes the characteristic and solemn tone of a manifesto addressed to mankind so that it may choose between two different paths and between two different concepts of "truth." In Bacon's view what was at stake was the closure of an epoch of civilization. His task was to assume the role of a herald pointing to a new human destiny, moreover, a role which was quite in keeping with his temperament. It seems to me that no "confirmation of fact" can ever eliminate, in any position of a pragmatist character, either this rejection of a certain mode of philosophizing, or this impassioned call for a choice between two kinds of "truth." To be sure, a twentieth-century philosopher like Dewey can refer, much more easily than Bacon could, to the recognition that science *in fact serves.* But Dewey also "rejected" classic logic by demonstrating the class character of culture in antique Greece,[38] and by his harsh disputation with

[38]John Dewey, *The Theory of Inquiry* (New York, 1938), esp. pp. 94ff. According to Dewey it is necessary to recognize the class structure of Greek culture. From this point of view, in consequence, classic logic "was partial even from the standpoint of the resources then and there available. The authors of the classic logic did not recognize that tools constitute a kind of language which is in more compelling connection with things of nature than are works, nor that the syntax of operations provides a model for the scheme of ordered knowledge more exacting than that of spoken and written language. Genuine scientific knowledge revived when inquiry adopted as part of its own procedure and for its own purpose the previously despised instrumentalities and procedures of productive works. This adoption is the radical characteristic of the experimental method of science." Interpreters have not dwelt sufficiently upon the Baconism which is no doubt one of the central aspects of Dewey's philosophy. See the article by G. Preti, "Dewey e la filosofia della scienza," already cited, which constitutes a significant exception. Much could be added to the argument, and it would not be difficult to demonstrate the close link between Dewey's position and Bacon's respecting, for example, the appraisal of Greek philosophy and civilization. Here it will suffice to recall how Dewey defines the program of the renewal of philosophy in *Reconstruction in Philosophy* (Boston, Beacon edition, 1957), p. 52. "Philosophical reconstruction for

those philosophies which view science as "a purely theoretical construction, in no way influenced by human aims or human needs." In Bacon's case, as in Dewey's, the thesis of an identity between truth and utility on the one hand, rests on a "confutation of the philosophies," and on the other, on an appraisal of technics and of the "mechanical arts" quite different from that peculiar to the classic world.

7.

In no way is it our intention to present the observations that have been made up to this point as a comprehensive interpretation of Bacon's philosophy and its historical significance. Our only purpose was to set off and illustrate some themes or thought motifs on which interpreters have not adequately dwelt within the complex tangle of positions and problems that constitute Baconian philosophy. These themes can be formulated as follows: (1) Bacon rejected the separation and the opposition of theory and practice, logic and operations, and truth and utility present in the ambit of the traditional philosophies (or of that which he maintained these philosophies were). (2) He interpreted this opposition as one bound to a twofold attitude (which according to him had precise and particular historico-social origins) of "veneration" for contemplation or for truth in its purity, and of indifference to, or "contempt" for, all that which is connected with practical or material operations.

---

the present is thus the endeavor to undo the entanglement . . . and to permit the Baconian aspirations to come to a free and unhindered expression." On Bacon as "the founder of modern philosophy," see in the same work pp. 28, 29, 37, 81. Here a characteristic passage of Dewey in *Problems of Men* (New York, 1946), p. 223, merits emphasis: "I am not quite sure, however, of the implications of certain forms of pragmatism. They sometimes seem to imply that a rational or logical statement is all right up to a certain point, but has fixed external limits, so that at critical points recourse must be had to considerations which are distinctly of an irrational or extra-logical order, and this recourse is identified with choice and 'activity.' The practical and the logical are thus opposed to each other. It is just the opposite which I am endeavoring to sustain."

(3) Hence he was concerned to take the opportunity to set off and illustrate the importance of material functions in the development of philosophy and culture. (4) On these bases he propounded and upheld the thesis of the identity of truth and utility, of theory and operations, and of knowing and making, and he arrived at the assertion that any separation or opposition imposed on these terms creates insuperable obstacles either with respect to the construction of "true" theories or with respect to the achievement of "effective" results.

The presence in Bacon's thought of theses of this kind should make it all the more problematic to speak, as is so often the case, of Baconian "utilitarianism." Moreover, they seem to conflict with the frequently repeated assertion of a "subordination" of science to technics, logic to operations, truth to utility, and learning to doing supposedly present in Bacon's philosophy.

Appendix III

The New Science and the
Symbol of Prometheus

1.

In the course of his studies on the Renaissance, Cassirer has laid great stress on the importance and significance of "concrete symbolical forms" in Renaissance philosophy. By demonstrating the shifts from the theme of Adam to that of Prometheus, most obvious in Boccaccio and Bovillus (Charles de Bouelles), he shed light on the ideals of humanity of which those symbols were the expression. The celebrated work by Seznec[1] and the studies of Charles Lemmi,[2] Renaudet,[3] and Yvonne Batard[4] have pointed to the importance which the "ancient fables" and the survival of the "gods of the Gentiles" had in the culture of the Middle Ages and of the Renaissance.[5] But, as has been rightly noted, the prominence accorded to the persistence of the contents and rhetorical conceits of the fables and

---

[1]J. Seznec, *La survivance des dieux antiques. Essai sur le rôle de la tradition mythologique dans l'humanisme et dans l'art de la Renaissance* (London, 1940); see also the review by Benedetto Croce in *La parola del passato*, III (1946), pp. 273–85, reprinted in *Varietà di storia letteraria e civile*, ser. II (Bari, 1949), pp. 50–65.

[2]C. W. Lemmi; *The Classical Deities in Bacon, a Study in Mythological Symbolism* (Baltimore, 1933).

[3]A. Renaudet, *Dante humaniste* (Paris, 1952).

[4]Y. Batard, *Dante, Minerve et Apollon: les images de la Divine Comédie* (Paris, 1952).

[5]See also M. Praz, *Studies in Seventeenth Century Imagery* (London, 1939).

symbols has prevented a general comprehension of the novelty of the attitudes and ideals which had found expression in these myths.[6] Thus Seznec, after demonstrating the presence of the myths of the classical world in the whole of medieval culture, used this ascertained identity of cultural contents to buttress the thesis of the strict and absolute continuity between the Middle Ages and the Renaissance. Renaudet and Charles Lemmi arrived at similar conclusions. Lemmi, who has demonstrated the derivation of Bacon's *De sapientia veterum (The Wisdom of the Ancients)* from the *Mithologia* by Natale Conti (replete with echoes of medieval culture), has declared that he is tempted to see in Bacon a medieval philosopher "haunted by a modern dream."[7] The equivocations which are born of investigations of this kind stem from a defective methodological formulation on which it would be useful to dwell briefly.

There is a type of historiography which believes it can determine the "significance" of cultural movements or thinkers of the past by availing itself of reductive formulas which are then elaborated into a theory of research. Such formulas eliminate as accidental and irrelevant all the historically concrete aspects of the various doctrines which do not lend themselves to such reduction. Thus historical investigation is reduced to setting off—hastily to be sure—the various "aspects of modernity," and to the routine job of assigning philosophers of the past to the slot that is necessarily due them within a "logical" frame, sketched *a priori*. Historiographers of this stamp, in general, reduce

[6]E. Garin, in connection with the investigations conducted by E. R. Curtius on the book as symbol ("Das Buch als Symbol," in *Europäische Literatur und lateinisches Mittelalter*), writes: "The absence of historicisation empties of any importance the whole investigation, which is reduced to an accidental enumeration of *examples* of the transferred use of the term *book*, where the very collection of *cases* never succeeds in becoming truly indicative, given the lack of a real perspective of the passages cited." E. Garin, *La cultura filosofica del Rinascimento italiano* (Florence, 1961), p. 451.

[7]Lemmi, *The Classical Deities*, p. 211.

history to the history of an epistemological problem, or simply to epistemology as such, so that they do not even bother to pose problems respecting the connections between a philosophical-historical or philosophical-cultural milieu.

Often, in a polemic with this first and rather monotonous form of historiography, many scholars have insisted on the necessity of tracking down the precise historical origins of the various conceptual positions. They have demonstrated the presence and persistence of cultural themes derived from tradition, in thinkers whom historiographers of the aforementioned persuasion, all too easily, hastened to qualify as "revolutionaries," or at least as the authentic precursors of the different revolutions. No doubt these pinpointed investigations have functioned as an effective remedy against the systematic falsification of those scholars who were exclusively concerned with tracing elements of an extraordinary modernity in all the thinkers of the past, from Heraclitus to Bruno. But often the upshot of this exclusive insistence on these enduring qualities and on the identity of cultural contents was to preclude any comprehension of the characteristics of novelty that were manifested each time that those cultural contents, in different situations, were interpreted in a different manner. Thus there was a real risk of putting on the same plane, Sappho, Dante, and Leopardi for the simple reason that all three wrote poems about the moon.[8] Moreover, after having demonstrated that the pagan gods had never died in the Middle Ages, such historiographers felt they were authorized to reduce all the possible allegorical interpretations to the common denominator "medieval," and to deny all differences of *form* and attitude which profoundly altered and modified the significance of those concepts derived from the medieval tradition.

It would be opportune to bear these considerations in mind where the intention is to avoid a twofold danger respecting the problem that interests us here. On the one

---

[8]E. Garin, *Medioevo e Rinascimento* (Bari, 1954), p. 72.

hand, we can limit ourselves to a Baconian interpretation
of the myth of Prometheus, that, where the characteristics
of novelty are not eagerly pounced upon, they can easily
appear as an expression of a marginal or accidental artistic
literary interest with respect to Bacon's "philosophy."[9] On
the other hand, through a concern to pinpoint the sources,
we can bridge every distance and at the same time empty
of meaning[10] the attempt—and one among the greatest—
to proclaim one of the ideals of modern philosophy and
science in the forms yielded by tradition and in the language peculiar to the epoch.

2.

From Hesiod to André Gide, the myth of Prometheus has
constantly accompanied the development of the cultural
consciousness of the West. An attempt to determine the
successive interpretations which have been given to this
myth would be tantamount to following, step by step, the
complex lines of that development. We are not setting ourselves such a vast task in these few pages. Our aim here is
to determine the elements of "novelty" which, with respect
to tradition, are present in the interpretation that Francis
Bacon gave to the myth of Prometheus and the meaning
that must be attributed to these elements with a view to a
general appraisal of the Baconian philosophy and of the
culture of the age of Bacon. The following brief references
to the history of the myth of Prometheus[11] consequently
serve exclusively the aforementioned aim.

[9]This, for example, is the conclusion drawn by V. F. Allmayer,
Saggio su Francesco Bacone (Palermo, 1928), p. 136.
[10]This is substantially the conclusion to which Lemmi's serious
and well-documented study leads.
[11]For the sources and the fundamental lines of this story, see O.
Raggio, "The Myth of Prometheus: Its Survival and Metamorphoses
up to the Eighteenth Century," *Journal of Warburg and Courtauld
Institutes* (1958), pp. 44–62; Darambert Saglio, *Dictionnaire des
antiquités grecques et romaines; Roscher, Ausfürliches Lexicon der
griechischen und römisches Mythologie;* Weiske, *Prometheus und*

In Hesiod[12] there is no trace of an attempt to justify Prometheus' rebellion; only in Aeschylus[13] does the bold appropriator of fire appear, who, for centuries, was to grip the imagination as the rebel who opposed the injustice and the tyrannous rule of the gods, who would not change his fate for that of servile Mercury and, who, for the love of man, gave him fire and taught him all the arts. From Prometheus men learned to build houses and to regulate their lives on the rhythm of the heavens; from him they learned mathematics, the alphabet, the art of taming horses, and of navigating the oceans; from him came medicine, the art of divination, and the ability to extract the precious metals hidden in the bowels of the earth. Furthermore, according to Diogenes,[14] Prometheus is responsible for having brought about the deep corruption of social life with the gift of the arts. In Plato,[15] Prometheus takes part for the first time in the creation of the human race.[16] By teaching men to honor the gods and to draw varieties of food from the earth, he thus in some way gave man "a share of the divine attributes."

In medieval culture Prometheus is no longer the rebel creator and is interpreted as a symbol of the one, divine creative potency: *"Deus unicus qui universa condit, qui hominem de humo struxit, hic est verus Prometheus."* This

---

sein Mythenkreis (Leipzig); and A. Kuhn, *Die Herabkunft des Feurs* (Ratisbona, 1854), have lost none of their usefulness. For the torch races, "Lampadedromia" in Saglio's *Dictionnaire des antiquités* and in Pauly Wissowa. On the interest that a history of the myth of Prometheus can present, see A. Gramsci, *Il materialismo storico e la filosofia di B. Croce* (Turin, 1949), pp. 166–68.

[12]*Theogony*, 507–610; *Works and Days*, 42–103.

[13]*Prometheus Bound.*

[14]Dion Chrysostom, *Logoi*, VI.

[15]*Protagoras*, 320, 321, 322b.

[16]Prometheus appears as the creator of men in *Philemon and Menandre* in Meineke, *Frag. comic. graec.*, vol. IV, pp. 32, 231; in Apollodorus, *Biblioteca*, I, vii, 1; in Ovid, *Metamorphosis*, I, 76ff.; in Juvenal, *Satires*, XIV, 34–35; in Maximus of Tyro, *Dissert.* XXXVI, I. See also Pausanius, *Periegesi*, X, iv, 4.

becomes the dominant theme in Tertullian,[17] Lactantius,[18] and Fulgentius,[19] and Prometheus now is the pagan travesty of the divine potency who, after creating man, breathes life into him. But in Servius[20] and Augustine,[21] besides being a symbol of divinity, Prometheus continues to be interpreted also as the "Reformer" who invented all the arts and the instruments of civil life.

"*Prometheus est philosophus*," writes Pomponazzi in *De fato*:[22] in the consciousness of the Renaissance, Prometheus becomes the symbol of the capacity for creativity which man alone, among all creatures, possesses. In Boccaccio[23] the theme we find present in medieval culture is combined with the glorification of Prometheus' creative power, and he interprets it according to a twofold symbolism: Prometheus is the true and omnipotent God who draws man into being; but Prometheus is also the man who inherited the power of his Titan father Iapetus, who abdicated in favor of his brother Epimetheus and found refuge in Assyria. Here in the solitude of Caos he studied the course of the stars, then came down from the mountains to teach men astrology and the ways of civil life. Thus men, "*rudes et ignari . . . agrestes et beluae*," were led from barbarism to civilization.

But it is in Bovillus, as Cassirer[24] has shown, that the myth of Prometheus becomes an expression of the individualism of the Renaissance. The wise man makes the *secondus homo*, the earthly man, out of the celestial man—the *primus homo*—the man of nature, and transforms a part into a whole, a beginning into a perfection, a seed into a fruit.

[17]*Apolog.*, 18, Adv. Marcion, I, 1.

[18]*Divin. instit.*, II, 11.

[19]*Mythologicon*, II, 9.

[20]*Com. in Virg. bucol.*, VI, 42.

[21]*De civitus dei*, XVIII, 8.

[22]*De fato* (Basilea, 1554).

[23]*Geneologie deorum gentiliun libri*, IV, *sub de Prometheo*. See the edition prepared by V. Romano, 2 vols. (Bari, 1951).

[24]E. Cassirer, *Individual and the Cosmos in Renaissance Philosophy*, tr. Mario Domandi (New York, 1946), pp. 96–97.

The wise man . . . imitates the famous Prometheus who, as the fables of the poets sing, after being admitted to celestial nuptial couches for a time, through a concession of the gods or through sharpness of intellect and wit, and after having attentively and thoroughly studied the celestial abodes found in them nothing more sacred, more precious and more fecund than fire. After stealing therefrom this element, which the gods vigorously refused to men, he introduced it into the world and with it he animated the man of mud and clay whom he had first formed. Thus also the wise man, forsaking the sensible world by dint of contemplation, and penetrating into the royal palace of heaven, drags into the terrestrial world the most resplendent fire of Wisdom conceived in the womb of the immortal mind, and through that pure and most fecund flame the natural and earthly man that is in him acquires strength, warms himself, and animates himself. The wise man compensates the gifts of nature with the actualization of the learned man; consequently, he acquires and possesses himself.[25]

The theme of the dignity and the central place of man in creation which we find in Pico, Manetti, and Ficino constitutes the meaning of Prometheus as conceived by Bovillus. Man is glorified not as a creature but as a thought, and man's privileged status in the world is not the fruit of divine will but of the free choice of man who has not been allotted a *nature*, as was the case with all other created things. Hence the nature of this man will be man making himself, as it were: and man's potentiality to make himself is infinite; its limits coincide with the limits of the universe. "And if the species which is called 'species of all' and that of natural man are the same, it necessarily follows that natural man must also be a potency of all, inasmuch as his act is an act of all, his species species of all, his image image of all, his number number of all. . . ."[26]

In the *De sapientia* the force of this reversal of the Stoic theme of man the microcosm risks being lost in a typical medieval idea structured in terms of rigid hierarchies and

[25]C. Bovillus, *De sapiente*, from the Italian translation by E. Garin (Turin, 1943), pp. 36–37.
[26]*Ibid.*, p. 94.

complicated analogic procedures. The Platonic inspiration of his *Lichtmetaphysik,* moreover, leads Bovillus to identify the sensible world. Hence by reattaching himself to Stoic themes he is led to accentuate the aristocratic and exceptional aspects of the figure of the wise man: "The wise man lives unmoved and impassable, for his proper, true, principle action, namely contemplation, is separated from the world, from time, from space, and from matter. . . . The mind of the fool, instead, maintaining itself empty, barren, otiose, and useless, never tries to rise to a higher world, never becomes equal to him. . . ."[27]

3.

What radically and primarily distinguishes every "modern" ideal of knowledge is precisely the renunciation of the concept of knowledge as contemplation and this final separation between wise men and fools—exceptional individuals endowed with mystical certitudes and the common run of minds. For Bacon (and perhaps also for Descartes) the problem was not to lead the human mind to the level of the divine mind or to contrive that the infinite reality of the universe be "mirrored" in the mind of the sage. Their exclusive aim was to liberate the limited intellect of men from prejudices, errors handed down by tradition—the "idols" which hinder and obstruct its normal functioning. Knowledge, according to Bacon, is not the product of the intuitions of solitaries, but the fruit of a thorough and radical reform respecting man's mode of thinking and speaking and which concerns the very structures of his societal coexistence.

An examination of the fundamental themes present in the Baconian interpretation of the myth of Prometheus will give us a concrete demonstration of this transformation of the ideals and tasks of knowledge better than would any discourse of a general order. Bacon had not read Bovillus'

[27]*Ibid.,* pp. 39, 51.

De Sapientia, but he probably was familiar with Boccaccio's
De genealogiis deorum (even though the comparisons that
have been made are not too convincing). The direct source
of his *De sapientia veterum* (as Charles Lemmi has amply
documented) was Natale Conti's *Mithologia.*[28] This work
ran through nineteen editions[29] in Europe between 1551
and 1627; together with the *Immagini* by Cartari,[30] and
the *De deis gentium* by Giraldi,[31] it became a kind of manual and source book on the myths of the classical world for
all the European intellectuals of that period. Also in his
twenty-seventh fable, of which Prometheus is the subject,
Bacon draws on Natale Conti's work without, of course,
ever mentioning him.

In Bacon's tale, Prometheus created the human race and
stole fire from heaven because of his love for man. Men,
however, were far from grateful toward their benefactor
and denounced him to Jupiter. In exchange for the denunciation, Jupiter left the possession of fire with the human
race and, as a reward, added the gift of perpetual youth.
The precious gift of the gods was loaded on the back of an
ass. On the way home the ass, tormented by an extreme
thirst, in exchange for a mouthful of water gave a serpent
who had been set to guard a fountain what he was carry-
ing on his back in payment. Prometheus meanwhile had
patched up his quarrel with mankind and had tried to de-
ceive Jupiter with a false sacrifice. As punishment for such
insolence, Jupiter ordered Vulcan to fashion a fair and
lovely woman called Pandora. The gods placed in her hands

[28]N. Conti, *Mythologiae sive explicationum fabularum libri decem*
(Venice, 1551).

[29]Three editions in Venice, four in Frankfurt, three in Paris, one
in Geneva, Lyons, Hassau, and Padua. In France, the translation by
J. de Montylard was published in Paris, Lyons, Rouen, and again in
Paris.

[30]V. Cartari, *Le immagini colla sposizione degli Dei degli Antichi*
(Venice, 1556). The work ran through 24 editions between 1556 and
1699, and was translated into French, German, and English.

[31]L. G. Giraldi, *De deis gentium varia et multiplex historia in qua
simul de eorum imaginibus et cognominibus agitur* (Basilea, 1548).

an elegant vase which contained all mischiefs and calamities. At the bottom of this vase lay Hope. When Pandora presented the vase to Prometheus he prudently refused to open it; but not so his ardent and impulsive brother, Epimetheus, and the result was that infinite evils flowed forth into the world. Jupiter, more wrathful than ever, because Prometheus had tried to ravish Minerva, condemned Prometheus to be bound fast to a column on Mount Caucasus, where an eagle gnawed and consumed his liver by day. The liver grew again at night so that the eagle could resume its torment of mankind's benefactor. Prometheus' cruel sufferings came to an end: Hercules, sailing across the ocean in an earthen pitcher given to him by the Sun, slew the eagle with his arrows and liberated Prometheus. Later, games called torch races were instituted in honor of Prometheus in which runners carried lighted torches in their hands. Victory went to the runner who reached the goal with his torch still burning.

Many of the truths contained in the myth, asserts Bacon, had already been clarified; others had completely escaped the majority of interpreters. According to tradition, Prometheus had created the human race. Thus he is the symbol of Providence, because the one thing that the ancients attributed to Providence, in the totality of things, was the creation of man. This was for two reasons: in the first place it seems incredible that the human spirit could have been derived from insensate principles devoid of intelligence; in the second place man, from the point of view of final causes, appears truly as the center of the world. The fire stolen by Prometheus is the origin of industry—of the mechanical arts and sciences through which man can modify his situation of original nakedness and defenselessness to make himself in some way the Lord of all created things.

Up to here the Baconian interpretation adheres to traditional models. Other episodes of the myth are interpreted by Bacon in terms of his philosophical and ethical-religious concerns. The episode relating to mankind's loss of the gift of perpetual youth indicates that antique medicine carried out attempts aimed at the prolongation of life, and that these attempts failed more because of the fault of men than because of the actual impossibility of this aim: the ass indicates "a sluggish and tardy experience" from which was born the ancient complaint that "life is short and art is long." Furthermore, it is a symbol of the nonactualized fusion of dogmatic and empirical philosophies: the sudden reconciliation of men with Prometheus alludes to the habit of backsliding, in a spirit of discouragement, from the old undertakings, that is, the reconciliation with tradition where new experiments would not have an instant success. Bacon uses the episode of Minerva, and that of the false sacrifice and of Hercules the liberator, to express some of the fundamental themes of his philosophy in the matter of religion: the attempt to ravish Minerva symbolizes the vain efforts of those who, puffed up with learning, claim to subject reason to divine wisdom; the false sacrifice indicates those rites and those ceremonies which serve the purposes of ostentation more than those of real piety. Hercules, who liberates Prometheus, is the image of the Redeemer who came down to earth in the frail vessel of human flesh in order to free the human race.

But Bacon does not just limit himself to an interpretation of the many episodes of the myth, leaving its traditional structure unchanged. He adds two episodes. The first is that of Hercules as the allegory of the Incarnation; the second is that of the ungrateful denunciation of Prometheus to Jupiter by the human race which had already received the gift of fire. It is precisely this part of the fable that appears particularly significant to Bacon: those who draw up an accusation and an arraignment against their own arts and their own nature are doing something that is more pleasing to the gods than those who glorify human nature and the learning in the possession of man. The latter are in a perpetual ecstasy before that which man possesses and, since they think they have arrived at the end of their efforts, they do not undertake or carry out any new investigations.

Only he who knows how to accuse and arraign man and human arts is impelled to embark upon new investigations, and to refuse to enslave himself spinelessly to a clique of arrogant philosophers. This is why the continuous doubts and perplexities of Empedocles and Democritus are to be preferred to the dogmatical philosophy of Aristotle who never doubts anything.

A certain interest should be attached to the fact that we find motifs in the chapter of a work, viewed as a literary exercise by the majority of interpreters, which were to be at the center of all Bacon's later work. Bacon availed himself of the myth of Prometheus in order to point to fundamental themes that were to be developed in the *Novum organum* and *De augmentis*. Actually, in a much harsher tone they had already been formulated in those youthful works which, for reasons of cultural expediency, Bacon felt he should leave unpublished.[32] But these themes are more or less familiar to every reader of the *Novum organum*: it would be opportune to pause here to consider a very significant passage in Bacon's *Prometheus* to show the deep difference that separates Bacon's Prometheus from that of Bovillus, in consequence of which we can measure the distance between the Baconian concept of science and the concept that was peculiar to the Renaissance:

The last point remains, namely the races with burning torches instituted in honour of Prometheus. . . . This again, like that fire in memory and in celebration of which these games were instituted, alludes to arts and sciences; and carries in it a very wise admonition, to this effect—that the perfection of the sciences is to be looked for not from the swiftness or ability of one inquirer, but from a succession. For the strongest and swiftest runners are perhaps not the best fitted to keep their torch alight; since it may be put out by going too fast as well as too slow. It seems however that these races and games of the torch have long been forgotten. . . . And well were it to be wished that these games in honour of Prometheus, that is of Human Nature, were again revived; that the victory may no

[32]*Temporis partus masculus, cogitata et visa, Redargutio philosophiarum.*

longer depend upon the unsteady and wavering torch of every single man; but competition, emulation and good fortune be brought to aid.

Not only does this theorization of the necessity of collaborative investigation as an essential component of science move on a plane very different from that which was typical of the philosophers and scientists of the Renaissance, but the very glorification of man, present in the Baconian Prometheus, assumes a very different meaning from this point of view. The concept of a man deprived of a particular *nature* and who can give to himself the nature that he wills, a concept on which Bovillus and so many others had forcefully insisted, remains substantially alien to Bacon's thought. Man's power is in no way infinite: he is *"obsessus legibus naturae."*[33] No human force can loosen or break the causal connections that regulate natural reality.[34] Hence man's task does not consist in the celebration of his infinite freedom, or of his substantial identity with the universe, but in becoming aware that the strengthening of the limited gifts of man requires an adequation to nature, a will to carry out her commands and to prolong her work. Only this will to adequation can permit the actual and not the illusory mastery of nature. Man becomes lord of nature only insofar as he is the servant and interpreter of this nature.[35] The human pretention to penetrate, with the senses and the mind, into the sphere of the divine is harmful and meaningless: the possibility of an *"operatio libera"* on nature points not to the possibility of operating all the modifications that are desired, but to the possibility of never encountering limits in those operations of transformation that know how to take account of natural laws that finally set themselves up as a prolongation of the work of nature.[36]

[33]*De int. naturae sent.*, XII, I.
[34]*Distributio operis*, at the end.
[35]*Novum organum*, I, 1.
[36]C. A. Viano, "Esperienza e natura nella filosofia di Bacone," *Rivista di Filosofia*, XIV (1954), p. 308.

INDEX

Académie des Sciences (France), 96, 97, 127–128
founded, 127
Academia de Cimento, L' (society), 96
Aconcio, Giacomo, 38
Advancement of Learning (Bacon), 118, 152
Aeschylus, 178
Agricola, 15, 16, 43, 50, 57, 59, 84, 103, 118, 128, 136
background of, 46–47
criticism of alchemy, 51–53
Agrippa, Cornelius, 54–55
Alberti, Leon Battista, 16, 19–20, 23, 24, 25, 32, 59
Alchemy:
Agricola's criticism of, 51–53
Bacon on, 87, 162–163
Biringuccio's polemic against, 44–45
Alembert, Jean Le Rond d', 134
Alsted, Henry, 128–129
Anderson, F., 150, 157, 164
Antal, F. 22
Aphorisma et consiliae (Bacon), 170
Apianus (geographer), 71
Apollonius, 17
Apologie (Hakewill), 92–93
Apprenticeships (artist), 21–23
Archimedes, 15, 17, 23, 57–59, 83, 146
Aristarchus, 17
Aristotelianism:
Bacon and, 85
definition of art, 137
nature-art relationship and, 137–138, 145

Cartesian philosophy and, 108–109
Aristotle, 13–14, 53, 55, 64, 73, 83, 125, 143, 147, 167, 185
Arsenius brothers, 38
Arte del navegar (Medino), 17
Art:
scientific progress and, 63–99
seventeenth century, 100–136
sixteenth century, 1–62
Atalanta, myth of, 163
Augustine, St., 101
Aurelius Augurelli, Johannes, 53
Averroes, 73

Bacon, Francis, 11, 15, 46, 108, 109, 117–121, 135, 136
on alchemy, 87, 162–163
on the Aristotelians, 85
death of, 122
on empiricists, 86–87
on form as *ipsissima res*, 158
knowledge of Latin, 157–158
mechanical arts and, 117–121
on nature-art relationship, 138–139
on fascination with antiquity, 84–85
reform program of, 80–87
scientific progress and, 64, 80–87, 99
sojourn in Paris, 2
Baconian philosophy, 146–173
distinction between speculative and operative natural philosophy, 167
empiricism and, 86–87, 163
heat and motion relationship in, 159

human mind "left to itself,"
159–160, 161
interpreters of, 149–151
logic and operations, 168–
169, 171
Mondolfo on, 146, 147–148
polemic against magics-al-
chemists, 162–163
Prometheus myth and, 181–
186
scientific truth question, 161–
162
sovereignty of man, 154
themes formulated, 172–173
truth and utility
affirmation of convergence
of, 161–172
identity, 151–160
Baillet, Adrien, 109
Baker, Mathew, 41
Banfi, A., 157
Barbaro, Daniel, 17, 60–61, 72
Barlowe, William, 16
Bartolomeus, 51
Batard, Yvonne, 174
Bauer, George, *see* Agricola
Bégue, Jean de la, 32
Belleforest, Fr. de, 65–66
Benedetti, 146
Bennewitz, Peter, 38–39
Besson, 16
Biringuccio, Vannuccio, 16, 43–
46, 52, 118, 128, 136
polemic against alchemy, 44–
45
Blondel, 98
Boccaccio, Giovanni, 174, 179,
182
Bodin, Jean, 74, 75, 99
Boileau, Nicolas, 91
Bonardo, Giovanni Maria, 50–
51
Borel, Pierre, 69, 89–90
Borough, William, 41
Bouelles, Charles de, 174, 179,
180–181, 182
Bourne, William, 41
Boyle, Robert, 3, 11, 15, 118,
121, 124, 125–127
universe concept of, 141

Briggs, Henry, 39–40
Browne, Sir Thomas, 143
Brunelleschi, Filippo, 15, 18,
22, 23
architectural constructions of,
33–34
Bruno, Giordano, 77–80, 100,
148, 176
Busson, H., 141

Campanella, Tommaso, 11–12,
65, 99, 100–102, 103,
104–105
Canfora, 157
Capitalism, 71
Cardano, Geronimo, 3, 55
Cartari, V., 182
Cartesian philosophy, 103–109
Aristotelianism and, 108–109
Leibniz and, 132–133
Cartier, Jacques, 66
Cartography, 38–41
Casa de Contratación (school),
39
Cassirer, Ernst, 174, 179
Castagno, Andrea del, 21
Cellini, Benvenuto, 15
Cena delle ceneri, La (Bruno),
77
Chambers, Ephraim, 135
Charles V, Emperor, 22, 47
Cicero, Marcus Tullius, 91
City of the Sun (Campanella),
100–101
Clocks, mechanical, 36
Cogitata et visa (Bacon), 155–
156, 166
Coignet, 38
Colbert, Jean Baptiste, 128, 136
Cole, 38, 41
Columbus, Christopher, 23, 101
Comenius, 99, 122, 129
Commandino, Federico, 17
Commentarii (Ghiberti), 18–19
Company of Mercers (London),
39
Compass, invention of, 82
Compositio hologuiorum (Mün-
ster), 17

Considé rations sur l'histoire universelle (Le Roy), 76
Considerations touching the Usefulness of Experimental Natural Philosophy (Boyle), 125–127
Conti, Natale, 182
Copernicus, Nicolaus, 78
Corsano, A., 103
Cowley, Abraham, 124
Crombie, A., 31–32
Cyclopedia (Chambers), 135
Cynics (philosophers), 147

Daniel, Gabriel, 141
Dante, 176
Da Vinci, Leonardo, 15, 24–29
  contempt for typography, 26
  elaboration concerns of, 27–28
  preference for mechanics, 146
Davis, John, 39
De antiquissima (Vico), 145
De augmentis (Bacon), 138–139, 166, 185
De causis corruptarum artium (Vives), 6
De deis gentium (Giraldi), 182
De dignitate et augmentis scientiarium (Bacon), 118
Dee, John, 39
De fabrica (Vesalius), 49
De fato (Pomponazzi), 179
De genealogiis deorum (Boccaccio), 182
De humani corporis fabrica (Vesalius), 7–8
De la vicissitude ou varieté des choses en l'univers (Le Roy), 76
Delineatio (Bacon), 163, 164, 165, 166
Delle fortificazioni (Lorini), 61
De magnete (Gilbert), 40
Democritus, 83, 153, 185
De natura fossilium (Agricola), 47
De ortu et causis subterraneorum (Agricola), 47

De proprietatibus rerum (Bartolomeus), 51
De prospectiva pingendi (Francesca), 20
De re metallica (Agricola), 47, 48, 49, 55
De revolutionibus (Copernicus), 78
De sapientia (Bovillus), 180–181, 182
De sapientia verterum (Bacon), 154
Descartes, René, 46, 136, 181
  on nature-art and machine, 139–140
  philosophy of, 103–109
De sensurerum (Campanella), 104–105
De tradendi disciplines (Vives), 5–6
Dewey, John, 171, 172
Dialogues Concerning Two New Sciences (Galileo), 112, 113–114
Diary (Bacon), 120
Diderot, Denis, 12, 128, 135, 136
Dieci libri di pensieri diversi (Tassoni), 87–88
Digges, Thomas, 38, 39
Dilthey, Wilhelm, 147
Diogenes, 178
Diophantos, 17
Discours admirables (Palissy), 1–4
Discours préliminaire (d'Alembert), 135
Discourse on Method (Descartes), 104, 105, 107, 132
Discourse touching the method of Certitude and the Art of Invention, 131
Discourses on Two New Sciences (Galileo), 62
Discourse of the Variation of the Compas, or Magnetical Needle, A (Borough), 41
Diverse et artificiose macchine

(Ramelli), 16, 59–60, 72–73
Donatello, Niccolò, 22
Donne, John, 68
Drury, John, 122
Duhem, Pierre, 24
Dürer, Albrecht, 16, 17, 27, 29

Edwards, John, 94–95
Elizabeth I, Queen, 38
Empedocles, 185
Empiricism, 66–68, 111
    Baconian philosophy and, 86–87, 163
Encyclopedia (Alsted), 128–129
Encyclopédie (Diderot), 12, 128, 136
Erasmus, Desiderius, 3, 5, 47
Euclid, 15, 16, 17, 83
Evelyn, John, 122, 124, 125
Expulsion of the Triumphant Beast, The (Bruno), 148

Fabricius ab Aquapendente, 47
Farrington, 43, 117
Ferdinard of Austria, King, 47
Fichten, John F., 34–35
Ficino, Marsilio, 180
Filander, 17
Filarete, Antonio di, 16, 20–21, 25
Fioravanti, 38
Fonsegrive, G., 150
Fontana, 16
Fontenelle, Bernard de, 91–92, 94, 97–98
Francesca, Piero della, 15, 20, 32
Francis I, King, 38
Frisius, 39
Frobisher, Martin, 39

Galen, 64, 139
Galilei, Galileo, 11, 17, 35, 36, 59, 62
    attitude toward technics, 112–116
    preference for mechanics, 146
Gassendi, Pierre, 98, 109, 112, 142

Gemini, 38
Gentile, Giovanni, 77
Ghiberti, Lorenzo, 15, 18–19, 22
Ghirlandaio, Domenico, 22
Gide, André, 177
Gilbert, Sir Humphrey, 9–10, 11, 39
Gilbert, William, 4, 40
Giraldi, L. G., 182
Glanvill, Joseph, 40, 93–94
Greene Forest, A (Mapler), 51
Gresham, Sir Thomas, 39
Gresham College, 39–40
Gunpowder, invention of, 82
Gymnasium mechanicum (school), 123–124

Hakewill, George, 92–93
Hartlib, Samuel, 122
Harriot, Thomas, 16, 39
Harvey, Gabriel, 11, 41, 130
Hauser, A., 22
Heraclitus, 176
Hero of Alexandria, 15, 17
Hesiod, 177, 178
Hester, John, 41
Hippocrates, 73, 83
Histoire des neuf rois Charles (Belleforest), 65–66
Hobbes, Thomas, 76, 98, 144–145
Homer, 91
Honnecourt, Villard de, 32
Hues, Robert, 16
Hugo of Saint Victor, 138
Humanism, 82
Huygens, Christian, 36, 104

Immagini (Cartari), 182

Jesuits, 12, 136

Kepler, Johannes, 35, 141
Keyser, Konrad, 15–16
Kigby, Sir Kenelm, 143
Koyré, Alexandre, 26, 32, 114

La Bruyère, Jean de, 13
Lactantius, 101, 179
La Mettries, Julien Offroy de, 141

Leibniz, Gottfried Wilhelm Von, 99, 105, 106, 108, 118, 132–133
  on Alsted, 129
  Cartesianism and, 132–133
  on image of God, 143–144
  mechanical arts and, 129–134
Lemmi, Charles, 174, 182
Lenses (eye), 35
Leopardi, Giacomo, 176
Le Roy, Louis, 66, 67–68, 76–77, 99
Levi, A., 150, 157
Liebig, Baron Justus von, 149–150
Lippi, Filippo, 21
Lenoble, R., 105
Locke, John, 13
Lomazzo, Paolo, 15
Lorenzo the Magnificent, 30
Lorini, 16, 61
Louis XI, King, 38
Louis XIV, King, 127
Louis XV, King, 90
Loyseau, Charles, 12–13
Luporini, Cesare, 29–30

Machiavelli, Niccolò, 41
Magia naturalis (Porta), 35
Manetti, Antonio, 18, 180
Maplet, John, 51
Marcomber, 125
Mariano, 16
Martin, Jean, 17
Martini, Francesco di Giorgio, 16, 32
Mastri sperimentatori (Olschki), 18
Maurice of Navarre, 72
Maurolico, Francesco, 16–17, 35
Mechanical Questions (Aristotle), 143
Mechanicorum libri (Monte), 16, 57–59
Medici, Cosimo de', 61
Medino, Pedro de, 17
Melanchthon, Philip, 47
Mémoirs mathématiques (Stevin), 72

Mercator, Gerhardus, 39
Mersenne, Marin, 69, 95–96, 98, 109–110, 144
Metallurgy, first printed book on, 43
Minera del mondo (Bonardo), 50–51
Mithologia (Conti), 182
Monantheuil, 143
Mondolfo, R., 146, 147–148
Montaigne, Michel de, 3, 13
Monte, Guidobaldo del, 16, 57–59, 60
More, Sir Thomas, 5
Moscovy Company, 39
Münster, Sebastian, 17

Nature-art relationship, 137–145
  Aristotelianism and, 137–138, 145
  Bacon on, 138–139
New Atlantis, The, 121, 122
Newe Attractive, (Norman), 4–5
Newton, Sir Isaac, 117
Norman, Robert, 4–5, 7, 11, 40–41, 136
Novum organum (Bacon), 2, 85–87, 155, 156, 157, 158–160, 165, 166, 170, 185

Ocean navigation, 39
  needs of, 36–37
Oldenburg, 97
Olschki, Leonard, 18, 112
Oxford University, 121–122

Palissy, Bernard, 1–4, 7, 11, 15, 128, 136
  scientific primitivism of, 3–4
Palladio, Andrea, 16, 17
Panofsky, Erwin, 29, 32–33
Pappus, 17
Paracelsus, Philippus Aureolus, 3, 55
Paralipomena (Kepler), 35
Parasceve ad historiam naturalem et experimentalem (Bacon), 118, 119
Pare, Ambroise, 71–72

Partis instaurationis secundae delineatio et argumentum (Bacon), 155, 163
Pascal, Blaise, 98, 99, 133
Patrizzi, 55
Peiresc, 69
Perrault, Charles, 90–91, 94, 127, 128
Petty, William, 12, 122, 123, 125
Philosophical College, 121
Philosophical transactions, 97
Philosophy:
  Bacon and, 146–173
  scientific progress and, 63–99
  seventeenth century, 100–136
  sixteenth century, 1–62
Pico della Mirandola, Giovanni, 180
Pirckheimer, Willibold, 71
Pirotechnia (Biringuccio), 16, 44, 143
Plato, 53, 61, 83, 91, 147, 153, 162, 178
Pliny, 125
Plus ultra, or the Progress and Advancement of Knowledge since the Days of Aristotle (Glanvill), 93
Plus ultra Reduced to Non Plus (Stubbe), 93
Plutarch, 57–58
Politiques d'Aristote, Les (Le Roy), 76
Pollaiuolo, Antonio, 21
Pomponazzi, Pietro, 179
Ponocrates, 7
Porta, Giambattista della, 35, 55
Praise of Knowledge, The (Bacon), 154
Principia (Descartes), 107–108
Printing press, invention of, 82
Prometheus, myth of:
  Baconian philosophy and, 181–186
  and cultural consciousness of West, 177–181
  in medieval culture, 178–179
  new science, 174–186

Prospectus of 1750 (Diderot), 135
Ptolemy (geographer), 17, 64
Pythagoras, 153

Quadrans astronomicus (Apianus), 71
Queen Elizabeth Academy (Gilbert), 9
Querelle des anciens et des modernes (Perrault), 90–91
Questions harmoniques (Mersenne), 110

Rabelais, François, 6–7
Raleigh, Sir Walter, 39
Ramelli, Agostino, 16, 59–60, 72–73
Randall, J. H., Jr., 26
Recorde, Robert, 39
Redargutio philosophiarum (Bacon), 85–86, 166
Reflections upon Ancient and Modern Learning (Temple), 94
Reflexions critiques sur Longin (Boileau), 91
Regulae (Descartes), 103
Renaudet, A., 174
Research organizations, beginning of, 96
Richelet, 12
Richelieu, Cardinal Armand du Plessis de, 13
Rimini, Valturio da, 16
Rivius, Walter, 17
Roberval, Giles Personne de, 98
Roriczer, Martin, 32
Rossi, Mario Manlio, 170
Royal Society (England), 93–94, 96, 97, 117, 118
  founded, 121–122
Royal Society (France), 127

Saloni, A., 157
Sappho, 176
Sarton, George, 26
Scholasticism, 42, 63, 168
Scientific primitivism, 3–4, 125

Scientific progress, idea of, 63–99
    Bacon and, 64, 80–87, 99
    Bruno and, 77–80
    research organizations, 96
    "technical" books written, 70–73
    use of *novus* (term), 70
Seneca, Marcus, 73
Seventeenth Century, 100–136
    Bacon and, 117–121
    Campanella and, 100–102
    Cartesianism, 103–109
    in England, 121–127
    in France, 127–128
    Galilean thought, 112–116
    Jesuits, 136
    Leibnizian writings, 129–134
    Mersenne and Gassendi, 109–112
Seznec, J., 174, 175
Sixteenth century, 1–62
    artisan contributions, 15–29
    awareness of methodological presuppositions, 42
    books on machines, 41–62
    cartography, 38–41
    collaboration between craftsmen and scientist, 29–41
    common themes, 10–15
    criticism of alchemy, 45, 51–56
    da Vinci and, 15, 24–29
    Jesuits, 12
    polemics against pedants, 1–15
    rise of bourgeoisie, 30–31
    royal patronage, 38
Socrates, 162
Sorbonne University, 1
Sortais, G., 150
Spedding, 157, 158
Sprat, Thomas, 122
Stevin, Simon, 16, 17
Strada, Giacomo, 43
Stubbe, Henry, 93
Sute, John, 41
Swift, Jonathan, 92

Tartaglia, Nicola, 16

Tassoni, Alessandro, 87–89
Teatro di macchine (Besson), 16
Technology:
    Baconian philosophy and, 146–173
    idea of scientific progress, 63–99
    seventeenth century, 100–136
    sixteenth century, 1–62
Telesio, Bernardino, 151
Telescope, invention of, 115–116
Temple, William, 94
Temporis partus masculus (Bacon), 166
Tertullian, 179
Testament politique (Richelieu), 13
Theophilus, 32
Titian, 22, 29
Torricelli, Evangelista, 114
Toscanelli, Paolo del Pozzo, 23
Truth and utility, 146–173
    affirmation of convergence in, 161–172
    identity and, 151–160

Uccello, Paolo, 21

Vartanian, 141
Vasari, Giorgio, 18, 22, 23
Versalius, Andreas, 7–8, 11, 15, 29, 48, 49
Verum factum, principle of, 145
Vico, Giovanni Battista, 74, 76
    principle of verum factum, 145
Vie treshorrificante du grand Gargantua (Rabelais), 6–7
Vier Bucher von menschlicher Proportion (Dürer), 71
Vigenere, Blaise de, 74–75
Virgil, 91
Vita di Brunellesco (Manetti), 18
Vitruvius, Pollio, 3, 15, 17, 19, 60, 72

Vives, Juan Luis, 5–6, 7, 11, 15, 128

Wilkins, John, 123
Wotton, Sir Henry, 124

Wotton, William, 94

Zilsel, Edgar, 40, 70–71
Zonca, Vittorio, 43
Zoubov, Vassili, 17

70 71 72 73   12 11 10 9 8 7 6 5 4 3 2 1

ABOUT THE BOOK

The text type for this book is Primer with display type in Baskerville. The book was composed by V & M Typographical, Inc. It was printed by offset and bound by Murray Printing Company, Inc.

Typographic designs by
C. Linda Dingler